PRAEGER INTRODUCTORY GEOGRAPHIES

France

Praeger Introductory Geographies

ITALY
J. P. Cole

SPAIN
W. B. Fisher and H. Bowen-Jones

HUMAN GEOGRAPHY
Emrys Jones

FRANCE

An Introductory Geography

by

E. ESTYN EVANS

FREDERICK A. PRAEGER, *Publishers*

New York · Washington

BOOKS THAT MATTER

Published in the United States of America
in 1966 by Frederick A. Praeger, Inc., Publishers
111 Fourth Avenue, New York, N.Y. 10003

The original edition of this book
was published in 1937
by Chatto & Windus, London,
and a revised edition was issued in 1959

Second Printing, 1967

© 1937, 1959, 1966 by E. Estyn Evans

Library of Congress Catalog Card Number: 66-17365

Printed in the United States of America

FOREWORD

By H. J. Fleure

Modern Geography has sometimes been called Human Ecology. It tries to show how men at varying stages in the growth or decline of civilization have grasped or neglected opportunities provided by their environment, and how in so doing they have both fitted themselves into its limiting conditions and often also fitted it to supply their needs. Sometimes immediate needs have been too insistent and the fitting in consequence has been temporary, the ultimate relations being impoverished by sacrifice to the short view. But in the case of "la belle France" we have to do with a land that has been loved and worked for many centuries, a land wherein a Roman inheritance, working upon Celtic and pre-Celtic local foundations, has been stimulated by the Frankish and Norse contacts which it latinized so remarkably.

No other land has such an intimate interweaving of almost all the contributions of the various peoples of Western Europe, and few, if any, other lands have such a deep social continuity, whatever the changes in politics and leadership may have meant. France is, in fact, the land that it behooves us to study most intimately if we are to follow the growth of a civilization impregnated with the idea of maintenance rather than expansion, of duration rather than temporary efflorescence, though both the idea of expansion and that of efflorescence have played notable parts in French life.

It is with these thoughts in mind that readers will, I hope, study this book by Mr. Evans, who has learned to think from a French as well as from a British point of view and to love the sunny land about which he writes.

CONTENTS

PART II: THE HUMAN BACKGROUND

ILLUSTRATIONS

MAPS

AUTHOR'S PREFACE

It is hoped that this book, written at the publishers' invitation, may prove useful not only to students of geography in high schools, colleges, and universities, but also to the wider body of those engaged in history or literature, whose studies may be enriched by a knowledge of the evolution of French life and landscape. It may thus contribute, in its modest measure, to the better understanding of a highly civilised nation.

In the book's arrangement a departure has been made from the old-fashioned method of attaching short historical and economic summaries to the geographical descriptions (or, in historical surveys, of dismissing the country's geography and pre-history in an introductory chapter); an attempt has been made to trace the physical and cultural evolution of the land and its peoples in Parts I and II and then, in Part III, to consider the present-day variety to which the past has contributed.

The regional maps have been specially drawn to include all names to which reference is made in the text: but they are not exhaustive or intended to take the place of a good atlas. Space for statistical lists could not be found in a book of this size. The student is advised to refer to annual publications, such as *The Statesman's Yearbook*.

The inspiration of Professor Fleure's teaching has helped me in innumerable ways, not least in enabling me to profit from the opportunities of travel that have come to me; and I owe a special debt of gratitude to my friend Mr. J. Bancroft Willans, under whose guidance in several extended journeys I have come to know nearly every corner of France.

I have been able to draw on the classic works and regional monographs of many French geographers, and I must acknowledge my indebtedness to Dr. Hilda Ormsby's book on France, a mine of information on the economic life of the country.

To Mr. Arthur Davies, of the University of Leeds, I am indebted for going through the proofs and making several suggestions; to my brother Mr. O. Tanat Evans for discussing with me the contents of Chapter 11; and to Professor D. L. Savory of the Queen's University of Belfast for reading that chapter and offering valuable comments on its substance. A former student, Mr. C. S. Cree, has kindly given me assistance in compiling the index.

E E E

NOTE TO SECOND EDITION (1959)

The text has been revised and statistics corrected from the French Census of 1954. Several of the maps have been redrawn by Miss Eileen Duncan.

NOTE TO THE AMERICAN EDITION (1966)

The text has been revised and statistics corrected. Chapter 22 has been re-written and the map on page 116 has been redrawn.

ACKNOWLEDGMENTS

The particular thanks of the author and publishers are expressed to Monsieur Charles Chauffard, President du Syndicat d'Initiative, E.S.S.I., for the pains taken to furnish the beautiful photograph of Vézelay, and to the Touring Club de France for that of Nancy: to Monsieur Camille Sauty of the Librairie de L'Enseignement for much assistance.

They are also much indebted to the following for permission to use the illustrations reproduced: MM. Bourelier (IVb); E. Michaud (IIa and Va); E. P. A. Moreau (Vb); Compagnie Aérienne Française (IIb and VIIIb); French Railways-National Tourist Office (IIIa, IIIb, VIIa and VIIb); and French Government Tourist Office (VIIb).

PART I

THE PHYSICAL BASIS

Chapter 1

INTRODUCTION: THE SETTING OF FRANCE

Thomas Jefferson remarked that every educated man has two countries, his own and France, and though politically her power has declined French civilization has been distinctive for many centuries. If we are to understand modern France we must look into the past in order to see how man's relations to his environment have changed more or less continuously down to the present day. The study of geography is greatly enriched if it concerns itself with these changes no less than with modern conditions. Its object must be to explain, but not necessarily to justify, the present. It will be our aim to view the life of France against the background of European civilization, to see it as possessing a strong regional personality within the common European cultural tradition.

The French Republic is the largest country in western Europe, having an area of 213,000 square miles, including the island department of Corsica. Its population (46½ millions) is less than that of Western Germany, and it is also exceeded by that of England and Wales, little more than a quarter its size. Internally, the natural units that make up the country include three great river basins, the Paris basin (Somme, Seine and Loire), the Garonne basin and the Rhône-Saône. These are set around a block of highland lying centrally in the southern half of the country and known as the Central Plateau, which is barely one-sixth of the total area of France; and although there are other important uplands, France is predominantly lowland, and agriculturally rich.

The High Alps form its south-eastern frontier; the Pyrenees its south-western. Between them, France fronts the western

Mediterranean, shared by the three great Romance countries (see Fig. 3). Northwards and westwards the country runs out into the Atlantic, and north-eastwards alone, between the Alps and the North Sea, is the frontier physically ill-defined and insecure, the result of complex historical processes. Here is Germany, flanked by Belgium and Switzerland. The land-frontiers of France measure 1,665 miles, the coast-line 1,760 miles, and the country might therefore be truly described as peninsular.

In France the world's standard meridian and the central parallel of the northern hemisphere (45°) cross each other. Both from west to east and from north to south the maximum distance is some 600 miles, between Ushant and Strasbourg, and between Dunkirk and Port Vendres. It is interesting to notice that these two lines of longest distance cross within a few miles of Paris. The extreme corners of the country, too, in the south-east and the south-west, are exactly equidistant from Paris (420 miles).

There is, then, a remarkable balance and cohesion about French territory. With this compactness of shape, France offers the easiest ways of communication between the northern and the southern seas of Europe; for the marginal lowlands of those seas meet in France as the mountain zone of central Europe dies away towards the west. The western Mediterranean and the Bay of Biscay come well within 250 miles of each other along a line (the Garonne valley) that continues the westward ways of the Mediterranean Sea. Here, between the Central Plateau and the Pyrenees, the two seas communicate with each other through the Gate of Carcassonne, whose grim walls still frown upon the historic route (Fig. 1).

Under the eastern face of the Plateau lies the long corridor of the Rhône-Saône, leading to the north over the low hills of the Côte d'Or. This corridor has echoed to the tramp of armies since Roman times, and it has witnessed wave after wave of civilization flowing from the Mediterranean. These two lowland ways, east and west of the Central Plateau, meet in the Paris basin to the north of the Plateau, and here they are joined by other focusing routes which come from beyond the Rhine, from central and eastern Europe. The ways along

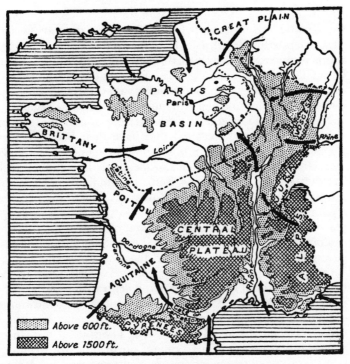

Figure 1 Relief and entries

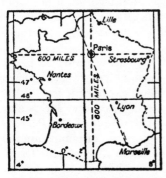

Figure 2 The symmetry of
France

Figure 3 Lands of Romance
Language

the Great Plain, interrupted on the west by the narrow seas that separate the British Isles from the Netherlands, are forced south-westwards and so lead through Belgium into the Seine basin. To the south, among the broken hills of south Germany, other routes lead from the Danube valley through the gaps between the Alps and the Ardennes, into the same region.

North France is therefore the western termination of several converging lines of movement that have their beginnings on the borders of Asia. And in this region these lines, which have associations with non-Roman Europe, come into contact with the shortest and easiest ways from the Mediterranean to the north, ways that are naturally Roman in their tradition. The region around Paris is thus fitted by nature to be a meeting-place and a melting-pot of peoples and of ideas.

The convergence of routes from the south and from the east gave this part of Europe—the part that was to become France—the possibility of participating from very early times in the life and thought of both southern and central Europe. As time passed, France came more and more to utilize its opportunities of sharing the experiences of Europe, and sometimes these experiences have taken a tragic turn. The sudden growth of power and population in Germany during the 19th century laid France open to expansionist movements across the Rhine. Within a hundred years she was thrice invaded by Germany and French fear of the overgrown industrialism of her neighbour has long been a serious difficulty in the way of international understanding. Her lead in promoting a European Community is understandable.

But France has other contacts which have affected her life at various times. On the south, besides her direct links with Mediterranean culture she has multiple connections with Italy by way of the Alpine routes and with Spain and Africa along the lowland avenue under the eastern end of the Pyrenees. In prehistoric times many southern species of plants, animals, racial-groups and cultures pushed north through this Iberian gateway and made their varied contributions to nature and life in France. Throughout history contacts along this "African avenue" have persisted.

At the western end of the Pyrenees another group of passes, in Navarre, has given access to the arid Meseta of Spain and to the wet coastlands of the Asturias and Galicia. A wealth of historic incident is concentrated in these passes, and the fame of Roncesvalles is enshrined in the traditions and in the epic literature of France. Here again the passes were in use before the dawn of history, and have long facilitated cultural exchanges within the Atlantic province of Europe—as in the pilgrim period and the age of chivalry.

There remain to be mentioned the contacts of France with the seas to the west and north. Both these seaboards have witnessed conflict with England and her maritime ambitions. They have their great ports with many overseas connections, and with memories of colonial expansion. In Brittany France possesses a fertile nursery of sailors, a great naval base (Brest), and a source of literary inspiration too; this ancient peninsula maintains its old ways, its Celtic language and its steadfast beliefs.

The gate of the Channel, from the Cotentin peninsula to the Straits of Dover, has seen many comings and goings and its connections are naturally with the south of England. The Northmen forced an entry along the Seine into the Paris basin, only to become "apostles of Gallic civilization". England took shape, in no small measure, under the stimulus of contact with France after the Norman conquest, and Britain in turn has made many contributions to French life.

With this diversity of outlook goes a remarkable capacity to absorb external influences. These multiple contacts have helped, throughout the centuries, to mould the French spirit and to make it a synthesis of European civilization. Internally the unifying process has been helped by the happy balance of her physical features. Here it must suffice to mention the main facts: the definite frontiers of mountain and sea on nearly all sides; the magnificent river system of the north with its centralizing influence; the river basins linked by lowlands or low hills and traversed by a great network of roads that owes its inception to Rome; the gradation of her varied regions one into the other, enabling them to share a large common measure of tradition; the wide extension of limestone rocks, which have attracted population from very early times, helped circulation and provided dry and usually fertile soils; the sunny climate and long attachment of man to gardening and agriculture, enriching life and contributing to the even film of population and to the continuity of social life from one generation to another.

It must be admitted, however, that the diversities of France have often led to disagreement and political upheaval. She has little of the British genius for compromise, so that adjustment to change has come by periodic revolutions which have not, however, broken the essential continuity of social life.

The material destruction suffered by France in the second world war amounted to about 40 per cent of her 1939 capital assets, but great efforts were made after 1945 to restore and strengthen the national economy and to encourage population increase. Nevertheless the divisions and weaknesses revealed by the German occupation of 1940–45 have not yet been fully healed. To many Frenchmen security and economic prosperity now seem to depend on the logical goal of Western European unity. France has taken the lead in promoting schemes for a Confederation of European States which would make a fourth war between France and Germany impossible. See p. 183. She has successfully undertaken the difficult process of decolonization, and with a population now increasing after a long period of stagnation, she has made remarkable progress in industrialization.

Chapter 2

STRUCTURE, RELIEF AND DRAINAGE

1 *Blocks and Folds*

The relations between geological formation and physical relief are well illustrated in France. We can distinguish clearly the river basins with their sedimentary rocks, the plateau regions composed of rigid blocks of old hard rocks, and the young mountains which run in vigorous chains folded against these relics of older mountains.

The continent of Europe was built up gradually from the north-west, and the shattered remnants of the oldest mountain lines, represented in Scotland and in Scandinavia, are not found in France. Southwards other lofty ranges were ridged up at the end of the Carboniferous period, and the frequently associated coal-measures of this Hercynian[1] system—as it is called—have contributed greatly to the wealth of modern Europe. While its general trend, like that of the later Alpine folds, was from east to west, it included, in what is now France, two great ranges converging southwards inside, and sub-parallel to, the present systems of the Pyrenees and western Alps. The ruins of these mountains can be traced from Brittany south-eastwards through the Gâtine, and from the Vosges south-westwards through the Morvan, meeting in the Central Plateau (Fig. 4).

In the course of long ages this old mountain system was reduced by denudation to a peneplain,[2] revealing the core of hard rocks—granite, gneiss and schist—which can be traced on the geological map. Other remnants of Hercynian mountains

---

[1] The name is derived from the classical word for the German forests. Many parts of these mountains are still heavily wooded, and the word "wald" (forest) often has the meaning of "hill country". Cf. Schwarzwald (Black Forest). The names Variscan and Armorican are also applied to certain sections of the system.

[2] A land surface worn by erosion to a fairly uniform level.

occur in the Ardennes plateau on the borders of Belgium; these beds dip westwards under later deposits in north-east France, but their presence here, as in east Kent across the Straits of Dover, is important because of the coal-measures they contain. In north Brittany, again, denuded ribs of the

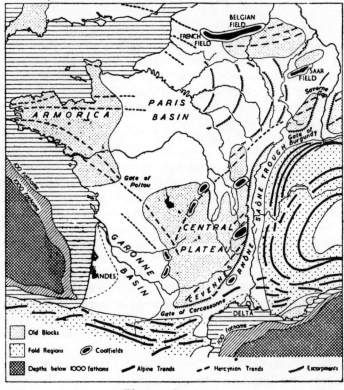

Figure 4 Structure

old folds run east and west, converging on the folds that reach south Brittany through the Gâtine.

In the Tertiary period, another phase of intense folding ridged up the floor of the warm sea (Tethys) lying to the south of the old mountains. This system, with its resistant rocks, acted as a rigid mass which checked and diverted the folds caused by the new earth-movements. The Alps, with their outer girdle, the Jura, folded by enormous pressure from the south against the Hercynian blocks, were forced to turn south-west and then south in front of the Vosges, the Morvan and the Central Plateau. Thus came into being the great curve of the western Alps.

The Pyrenees, the other "fold-frontier" of France, also owe their character to local conditions. They were restricted not only by the Central Plateau but also by the more massive block of the Spanish Meseta, and they show this restriction in their regularity, their high average elevation and straight alignment.

2 *The Central Plateau and the Vosges*

But while the older system, thanks to its rigidity, was not involved in the new folding movements, it suffered severe fracturing and vertical displacement. The Central Plateau, its main nucleus, was tilted towards the north and north-west, away from the stress of Alpine pressure. Its main drainage, in consequence, goes in these directions, a fact of considerable importance in the life of France. The upper Allier and Loire, flowing north, occupy a series of basins let down between parallel sets of faults. The western side of the plateau is drained by tributaries of the Garonne, occupying fault zones caused by, and running parallel to, the Pyrenean folds.

Another result of the intense fracturing was a great outburst of volcanic activity. Successive streams of lava added height to the Velay and Cantal regions (about 6,000 feet) and a string of volcanoes made its appearance along the west side of the Allier. This phase continued long after the Alpine folding had ceased, and some of the volcanoes may have been active in early human times.

The raising and fracturing of the Hercynian blocks is well illustrated in the Vosges and the Black Forest, which must originally have formed a continuous block, but a central strip subsided between sets of parallel faults to form the Rift Valley of Alsace. The sharp up-thrust edges of the Vosges and Black

Forest now face each other across the depression, which, with its broad marsh-lined river, has been, since Roman days, one of the most famous frontier-zones of Europe.

3 *The Rhône-Saône*

The relations between block and fold also give south France its two great river basins, the Rhône-Saône and the Garonne. There are many interesting differences between these two valleys, but they both occupy structural troughs between block and fold, lying under the edges of the Central Plateau just as the Ebro and the Guadalquivir are under the Spanish Meseta. And as the Spanish rivers flow in opposite directions one to the Mediterranean and the other to the Atlantic, so the Rhône and the Garonne drain respectively south and north-west.

The narrow valley of the Rhône, below Lyon, continues the broader basin of the Saône, the whole forming a long corridor and providing a famous way of communication and of civilization. To the west is the broadly continuous line made up of the scarped edges of the Cévennes, the Lyonnais mountains, the Côte d'Or and the Plateau de Langres. This wall becomes progressively lower and narrower as one goes north from the Cévennes, and the older rocks sink, between the Morvan and the Vosges, under later (Jurassic) deposits in the Plateau de Langres, over 1,000 feet but often below 1,500 feet in height. Into these deposits the headstreams of the Seine and its tributaries have cut, so that there is no serious obstacle to easy communication from the valley of the Saône to the Paris basin. These passages were the heart of historic Burgundy, the nucleus of which sat astride the Côte d'Or.

South of the granitic Morvan another weak belt, this time eroded from north-east to south-west, offers a passage between the Saône and the upper Loire, and several important lines of communication are concentrated in this gap.

The Saône basin is prolonged towards the north-east by the depression between the Vosges and the Jura, which is known as the Gate of Burgundy or of Belfort. It opens northwards into Alsace and eastwards past Basel, where France meets Germany and Switzerland, into the Alpine foreland. The Jura and the

Alps, sweeping in a gentle curve from Basel down to Marseille, flank the Rhône-Saône basin on the east; and midway along this curve the tortuous and often turbulent Rhône brings in the drainage of south-west Switzerland. The other river feeders are also on the Alpine side; Doubs and Ain from the Jura, Isère and Durance from the High Alps. These mountain rivers, notably the Rhône, Isère and Durance, carry enormous loads of silt which go to build out the delta.

4 The Mediterranean Coast

Below Valence the Rhône valley widens gradually as the Cévennes and the Alps diverge, and a broad triangle of low-land terminates in a flat lagoon-lined coast curving in a cres-cent between Agde and Marseille, with the broad projecting delta of the Rhône set midway between. The plains west of the river, under the Cévennes, make up Languedoc, a sunny region facing south-east. On the left bank of the river is Pro-vence. On this side the lowland gives way fairly soon to the hills, and east of Marseille the mountains are everywhere near the sea.

Beyond Toulon the coast turns east and then north-east, and breaks up into numerous promontories. This indented coast gives way to a more regular coast as one leaves France and passes, beyond Mentone, into Italy. The south-western part of the Riviera (as this tract is called) is composed of shattered remnants of an old block, folded in Hercynian times, which once embraced Corsica and Sardinia. The geological map shows these areas to be composed largely of Archaean and Primary rocks. In Provence, the Chaîne des Maures, between Fréjus and Hyères, is the most distinctive fragment; its imper-meable rocks give the whole countryside a character of its own. The Iles d'Hyères are also portions of the same former land-mass. This old block turned the Alpine folds eastward much as that of the Central Plateau turned them southward. Thus we have a sharp eastward bend of the Alps in Provence.

5 The South-West

The western lowlands of south France are separated from the Mediterranean by a projecting angle of the Central Plateau

known as the Montagne Noire, between which and the
Pyrenees is the narrow but low and easily accessible Gate of
Carcassone. The broad basin of Aquitaine, floored by upper
Tertiary deposits (gravels, sands and clays) and by patches of
alluvium, takes the shape of a triangle with its apex not far
from Toulouse and its base on the Bay of Biscay, where it ends
in the straight current-swept dune-coast of the Landes.

Some of the drainage of the Pyrenees goes separately to the
sea by the Adour, but most of the rivers of the basin, from the
Pyrenees as well as from the Plateau, combine to reach the sea
in the Gironde. On the east they form a remarkable series
(Dordogne-Lot-Aveyron-Tarn) cutting deep gorges through
limestone plateaux which were carried up with the hard core
of the Central Plateau when it was raised by the Alpine
pressure. The southern feeders of the Garonne flow through an
enormous fan of gravels and clays brought down from the high
central Pyrenees; the upper Garonne itself is the easternmost
of this series of streams.

The Garonne basin in turn communicates with that of the
middle Loire around the north-western flank of the Plateau,
where the low Gate of Poitou forms a limestone bridge connecting the two basins and separating the granites of the
Limousin from those of the Gâtine. The middle Loire region,
between Nevers and Angers, is in every way a part of the
Paris basin and the tributaries are uniformly from the south,
i.e., from the Central Plateau. Although the Loire itself drains
to the Atlantic, yet the river is so placed that it enriches rather
than detracts from the unity of the Paris basin.

6 *The Paris Basin*

This region may be briefly described as occupying the depression between the old blocks of Brittany, the Ardennes and the
Central Plateau. Unlike the Garonne and Rhône-Saône basins
it is not flanked by fold mountain chains on one side. Its highland rims are all of the same general type (though Brittany
is lower than the others) and this gives the basin a unity and
balance that the others lack. It thus differs essentially from the
two basins of south France in being flanked by comparable

structural elements, of roughly similar height, on all sides, without the sharp contrast between old block and high folds framing triangular troughs, whether broad or narrow.

Its sedimentary rocks are arranged in concentric rings, with the youngest inside. The most complete and characteristic of these rings is the Cretaceous. Towards the higher rims of the basin Jurassic rocks outcrop against the plateau of Lorraine on the east, and against the granites and schists of the Morvan and Limousin on the south-east and south. Sedimentary rocks form the sills or gates by which the basin communicates with the southern lowlands and with the Great European plain through Artois.

The component parts of this richly varied region owe their geographical unity chiefly to the river system. The Seine and its tributaries drain almost the whole of the eastern half of the basin; they come together for the most part towards the centre of the latest (Tertiary) beds; and Paris, which gives its name to the basin it has long dominated, occupies a site near the point of greatest concentration. River erosion acting upon alternating belts of hard and soft rocks has produced the famous series of limestone plateaux and clay vales. These low plateaux are tilted slightly towards the centre and their outer faces form escarpments, so that the whole structure has been compared to a nest of saucers.

In the north, the drainage of the Cretaceous deposits goes independently to the Channel by the Somme and other streams. But beyond the Artois ridge the head-waters of the Belgian streams—Lys, Scarpe and Sambre—follow the slope down towards the Brussels basin, and France gives way to Belgium as the chalk passes under sands and clays that form a continuation of those in the London basin.

7 *The West*

The country lying to the west of the Paris basin, with its twin peninsulas—Brittany and the Cotentin—is a region apart: Armorica. Its convergent Hercynian folds were worn down long ago to form a peneplain which was fractured and raised at the time of the Tertiary folding. But because of its comparative remoteness it suffered neither the intense fracturing nor the vulcanism of the Central Plateau. The highest point, in the Monts d'Arrée of Finistère, is but 1,300 feet.

Brittany is essentially a low plateau whose surface is diversified by the harder ribs of granite, schist and slates standing out above the eroded softer beds of shales and clays. The latest movement has been a subsidence, so that it has many drowned estuaries and fringing islands on all sides.

8 *The East*

Balancing Brittany on the east of the Paris basin, but lacking to its sorrow the fixed frontier of the sea, is the region known to history as Alsace-Lorraine, drained by the Rhine and its tributaries, Meuse, Moselle and Saar. Alsace (lying on and under the Rhineward slopes of the Vosges), together with parts of Lorraine, form one structural unit, but most of Lorraine comes into the scarp-system of the Paris basin. Its rivers, however, have been diverted to the Rhine and cut deep trenches to the north and north-east. Between these scarps and the High Vosges is a belt of clays and salt-bearing sandstones. Lorraine thus shows considerable geological variety which is reflected in the mineral and agricultural wealth of the Moselle and its tributaries.

The High Vosges rise in a series of terraces to the crystalline core, reaching a height of 4,750 feet in the "Ballons". A depression separates them from the Low or Sandstone Vosges to the north. This depression (the Col de Saverne) is caused by a river working along a fault zone to the north-west of Strasbourg. It forms a highly important connecting link between the Rhine and lands to the west.

Chapter 3

ROCKS AND SOILS

1 *Limestones and Loess*

The geology of a country, besides bearing a direct relation to the relief, profoundly affects the life of man because of the mineral content of rocks, their permeability or impermeability and their fertility when weathered into soils. It also helps to determine many other factors in the physical environment. We shall consider some of these factors and their distribution in this chapter.

France is essentially an agricultural country, and many features of her civilization are derived from this fact, which depends, in turn, to no small extent on the fertility and the variety of her soils. Only in three isolated regions—Brittany, the Central Plateau and the Vosges—are the very old and usually infertile crystalline rocks predominant. And the largest of these—the Central Plateau—which occupies as we have seen only one-sixth of the area of the country, is diversified by recent volcanic rocks and by fertile fault-basins such as that of the upper Allier.

A clue to the agricultural wealth of France is to be found in the fact that two-thirds of its surface is floored with limestone, whether Jurassic, Cretaceous or Tertiary. These limestones may form great mountain lines, as in the Jura and parts of the Alps and Pyrenees, or high plateaux, as in the *Causses*, or again low plateaux, as in the basins of Paris and Aquitaine. They are varied in their composition and texture, but they are all alike in their dryness, their deep dissection by river valleys, and their suitability for cultivation wherever altitude or drought do not interfere.

The limestones form the wheatlands of France, and often the vineyards, for the vine prefers light soils. The high plateaux provide summer pasturage for cattle and sheep. The low plateaux are best developed in the Paris basin, where they are frequently capped by clay or loam (*limon des plateaux*) closely related to the wind-blown loess soils of central and eastern Europe. These loams, with their well-drained subsoils, constitute the rich corn-lands of the Paris region, and have contributed to the wealth and power of north France since they were first cultivated long ago.

Because of their continuity from Languedoc to Picardy and from Lorraine to Saintonge, the limestones have acted as connecting-links between the Mediterranean and the English Channel on the one hand and between Central Europe and the Atlantic on the other. Being dry and not heavily forested, even in prehistoric times, thanks to their porosity, they have provided avenues of migration westwards from the Jura, northwards from the Mediterranean and also westwards along the Pyrenees into Asturias. A famous series of caves of Palaeolithic (old stone age) man in south France and north Spain testifies to the very early utilization of these limestones.

The Celtic migrations from Central Europe were guided by exposures of dry limestone soils, while the Romans drove their straight roads with ease across the low plateaux of the north, and *Durocortorum* (Reims) in its open *champagne*,[1] became one of the chief road-centres of Gaul. The modern highways, of which France is justly proud, and which have grown out of the post-roads organized by Colbert in the 17th century, also make considerable use of these plateaux.

Moreover, the gate of the Channel, from the Cotentin to the Boulonnais, is paved with limestone—mostly chalk—and France's many connections with England have been largely concentrated in this zone, opposite which natural piers of similar formations are thrust into the Channel between Portland Bill and the North Foreland. From Boulogne to Dover and from Dieppe to Newhaven the cross-channel boats ply between coasts of chalk.

The limestones also serve as reservoirs of water, nourishing settlements along the spring-lines where streams emerge under

[1] Compare the English "champaign", "champion", referring to an expanse of open country.

their scarped edges, and supplying great cities like Paris itself. Nor should we omit to mention the importance of these rocks in providing the excellent building stone that has helped to

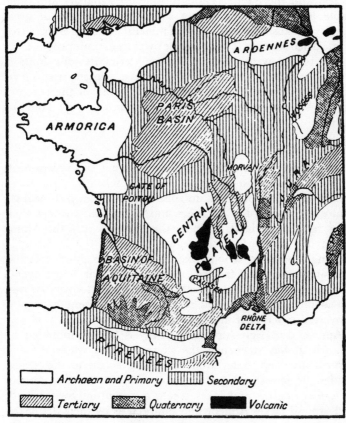

Figure 5 Geology

make France an outstanding centre of architecture from Roman times onwards. The quarries of Caen exported their freestone to many places in England during the Middle Ages.

Reference has been made to the loess often found as a thin surface layer in the Paris basin. Similar soils occur in Alsace, and in parts of the Rhône and Garonne basins.[1] To these rich agricultural soils we must add the alluvium of the great rivers and the deposits of old lake-basins like the Limagne (upper Allier) and the Saône. Though sometimes marshy and often liable to floods, these young soils are frequently of great fertility because of the mixture of mineral elements transported from varied sources. The Limagne owes its famous productivity partly to the weathered volcanic material its soils contain. Along the large rivers, the gravel terraces provide useful level sites for settlements and communications out of the reach of floods. A good example of this is to be found in the Toulouse district.

2 *Glaciation*

In most parts of northern Europe the legacy of the ice-sheets of Pleistocene (post-Tertiary) times is felt in many ways. France lay south of the main zone of glaciation, but local ice centres existed in the Pyrenees and in the Alps, where their relics remain as glaciers. Under the southern Jura the Alpine ice has left its mark in the region known as the Dombes, in the angle between Rhône and Saône, where thick irregular deposits brought by the ice cause imperfect drainage over a wide area. Marshes and meres made this region long malarious, but artificial drainage and scientific management have now converted much of it into productive pastoral land.

Among the High Alps the scenery is largely moulded by ice, which has steepened the slopes, caused waterfalls and carved out deep valley trenches giving access to the passes. Under the ice-scored granite mass of Mont Blanc a number of tourist centres and lakes create a miniature Switzerland; and around Lakes Annecy and Bourget, as by the Swiss lakes, prehistoric man found suitable conditions for building pile-dwellings. There are no large lakes in the Pyrenees, but glaciated features are abundant. The well-known cirque of Gavarnie is ice-cut, and glacial ledges and U-valleys with hanging tributaries tumbling over waterfalls into the main stream are common.

Compare Fig. 10, p. 58.

3 *Minerals*

France has, in Lorraine, the largest reserves of iron-ore in Europe, and her production of pig-iron now ranks second only to that of the U.S.A. The ores, known as *minette*,[1] occur between the middle and lower Jurassic deposits, underlying the Oolite. This iron-field, and the coal-field of the Belgian border, are the most extensive mineral regions of France; they are both near her frontiers, and neither can be considered typical of the country. What we have, in general, is a number of small scattered fields. From this it follows that there is not the top-heavy concentration of large industries and populations in localized areas that we find in Britain and Germany. Many features of the social life of France are related to this geographical fact. She has remained a country of small cities, which have often kept their old industries and serve the agricultural regions round about; and the fertility of her soils has enabled her to maintain a balance between urban and rural populations and to keep to a great extent the self-sufficiency which we in Britain have lost.

The small coal-fields of France, which are related to the exposures of older rock, occur mainly at the edges of the Central Plateau and include those of Le Creusot-Blanzy, St. Etienne, Alais, Carmaux, Commentry and Brassac. They are preserved in Hercynian down-folds and fissures, as their orientation from north-east to south-west suggests, and the beds are usually disturbed and difficult to work. Their output is small, some producing annually only about half a million tons. Between the end of the war of 1914–18 and 1935 the output of the Saar coal-field went to France. As the result of a plebiscite (Jan. 1935) the Saar became German territory once more. It was under French occupation (1945–57) but is now a *Land* of the German Federal Republic.

Although the enormous iron-field of Lorraine today produces 95 per cent of the total output of French ore, we find that the iron industry has in the past been located in numerous small centres scattered throughout the country, all formerly

[1] See note on p. 119.

dependent on local ores though some now import from Lorraine. Local supplies of charcoal, as in Berry, Nivernais and the Jura, helped to fix the industries, while the presence of water-power was formerly a factor. The coal-fields of Le Creusot and St. Etienne have ensured the development of some of the iron industries of the Centre, and hydro-electric power has helped production, e.g., in the Pyrenees. France's output of aluminium (350,000 tons) exceeds her national needs. Oil is produced under the Pyrenees at Lacq, where natural gas is refined and piped over ever-increasing distances. Sulphur is an important by-product of the refineries, and the French chemical industry has expanded rapidly. More recently an important oil-field has been exploited at Parentis in the Landes, and atomic power-stations are being developed, particularly in the Loire Valley.

Salt is a common mineral which has long had many uses. It was laid down under desert conditions and is sometimes found with Triassic deposits, as in Lorraine. Only in the Saulnois between Nancy and Metz is it exploited to any extent (for France gets most of her salt by evaporation from sea water), but it was formerly utilized in several parts of the country. Salins and Lons-le-Saunier in the Jura (the Roman *Salona* and *Ledo Salinarius*) owe their names to the industry. In pre-Roman times the salt springs of Lorraine, the Jura and the Pyrenees attracted populations interested in agriculture, for salt is required with a cereal diet and probably salted meat was already used for winter food.

In the days before iron was worked it was the precious metals, gold, copper and tin, that were sought after by man; and these must be looked for among the old blocks with their intrusive granites. In the west, while some gold was probably won from the *Ariège*—it was panned in the Garonne valley until last century—tin was certainly obtained and must have played its part in attracting the early maritime civilization of Brittany (see Chap. 7).

We have seen how the influence of geology and soils upon vegetation is one of the many links between nature and man. Vegetation and crops are also related, however, to climate, and we must now turn to the climates of France.

Chapter 4

CLIMATE

1 *Variety of Climates*

The climates of France, no less than the structure and soils, are distinguished by their variety. The three sub-divisions of European climate commonly recognized—maritime, continental and Mediterranean—are all met with, and France is the only country of which this is true. In climate as in all her external relationships, France is influenced by the Atlantic, by central Europe and by the Mediterranean. Internally, the altitude and distribution of the mountain masses are the chief controls.

The north and west are regularly in the track of the variable westerly winds; the rainfall is well distributed through the year, with a maximum fall in autumn, when the sea winds are heavily charged with warm water-vapour and the land is cooling rapidly. But only where relatively high land approaches the sea, as in parts of Brittany (over 40 inches) and especially under the western Pyrenees (over 60 inches), is the rainfall high. Between the mouths of the Loire and the Garonne, the low coast has less than 30 inches, i.e., much the same as most of the Great European Plain and east central Europe.

Although so largely under the influence of the Atlantic, then, France does not show, as do Britain and Scandinavia and the Iberian peninsula, that enduring contrast between a wetter west and a drier east which has meant so much, for example, in the life of Great Britain. Indeed, the areas of heaviest rainfall occur, with the highest relief, in the Central Plateau, the Morvan and the Vosges, where their continuity is broken by many sheltered river basins. The Pyrenees and Alps, because of their height, are very wet except where they border the Mediterranean, but the Spanish side of the Pyrenees is dry.

35

2 *Pressure*

In winter, the mountain belt of the Jura, Alps and Central
Plateau tends to have high pressures, often extending to link
up the Azores "High" with the great continental anticyclone
of Asia. To north and south of this "barometric backbone",
winter pressures over the British Seas and over the Mediterranean are normally low, and cyclonic storms are frequent.
The cyclones of the notoriously stormy Bay of Biscay, though
they may sometimes penetrate into the Mediterranean by the
Gate of Carcassonne, are for the most part drawn north-
eastwards along the English Channel. The Gulf of the Lion,
as its name suggests, can be very rough in winter. Here and
in Mediterranean France as a whole the rain comes from
cyclones of local origin, which usually cross the western
Mediterranean basin. In so doing they may either cause wet
on-shore winds or draw down cold air from the Cévennes and
the Alps—the Mistral.

With the approach of summer the main pressure belts move
northward as the sun's influence migrates. The Asiatic "High"
is replaced by a low-pressure system, and during the change-
over the higher parts of the Alpine mountain-belt receive
heavy rains. The cyclone tracks now run farther north, and
the depressions are fewer and milder. The rainfall that comes
to central and eastern France in summer is mostly due to
thunder showers caused by local overheating and convectional
overturnings of masses of air.

The Mediterranean coasts, too, receive rain at the change
between winter and summer conditions, but the spring is short
and by May the dry summer is established. South Europe is
now a region of relatively high pressure from which dry
northerly winds blow out to join the north-east trades across
the Sahara.

The dominating summer pressure system, however, is the
Azores anticyclone, which tends to spread over the Iberian
peninsula and south-west France; thus the low west coast from
the Morbihan southwards gets only light summer rains and
has a high sunshine record, though the heat is tempered by
the relative coolness of the waters of the Bay of Biscay. In the

angle of the Bay, along the western Pyrenees, while the maximum fall (as in most of France) comes in autumn, there may be heavy rains in summer, but the storms pass quickly and the sky is bright if changeful.

The centre of the basin of Aquitaine is dry in summer, and the Paris basin, though it gets a fair amount of rain, is definitely dry in the region of the middle Loire. Rainfall increases with elevation on the east side of the basin (diminishing again in Alsace) and towards the sea on the north and west.

3 *Annual Rainfall*

Reviewing the distribution of precipitation in an average year (see Fig. 6) we may say that the wettest districts are the regions of high relief in the south, centre and east, and the areas of moderate relief along the Atlantic coasts (i.e., Brittany and the Cotentin). The main river valleys stand out as regions of low rainfall, notably the rain-shadow areas of the Paris basin, the middle Rhine, and the Limagne and Forez basins (upper Allier and Loire) slotted into the Plateau. In addition the lowlands of the Mediterranean coast, east of the Pyrenees and around the Rhône delta, have little rain.

Yet no part of the country has less than 20 inches. France's agricultural wealth is closely bound up with these regions of adequate but light precipitation; and the fact that they are found so widely scattered around the Central Plateau in all parts of the country has greatly facilitated the growth of common interests between the main lowland centres of settlement.

4 *Temperature*

Intercourse has been encouraged, too, by the diversity of the products of these lowland regions, which have certain climatic characteristics which enhance the rich variety of nature. A consideration of temperature will throw light on these. Within the unity of the temperate climate natural to a land facing the western ocean between latitudes 43° and 50°, there is the distinction between a cooler north and a warmer south. This distinction breaks down somewhat in winter, despite the

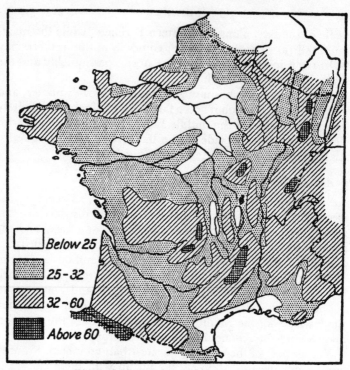

Figure 6 Annual rainfall (in inches)

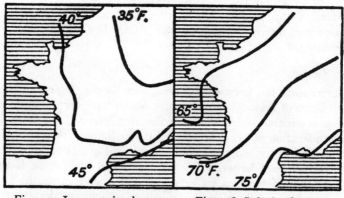

Figure 7 January isotherms   *Figure* 8 July isotherms

renown of the Riviera for winter warmth, but the fact remains that the south derives much of its character from its warmer, sunnier climate; and we have this in mind when we speak of the "Midi".

South of latitude 46°, the sun's rays at mid-summer are only some 20° from the vertical. The July isotherms run roughly east and west, but they bend southwards towards the west under the cooling influence of the sea. The 65° line approximately follows the north coast; that of 70° runs from about Biarritz to Lyon, so that the Rhône valley is hotter than the Garonne; the 75° isotherm follows the south coast, and only Roussillon is warmer still.

In winter the isotherms tend to run from north to south, influenced by the cold heavy air of the continental anticyclone and by the relative warmth of the Atlantic. The whole of the country is well to the west of the 32° line, an important line in European life. Most of Germany lies within this line, which means that January (east of the River Weser) is normally a frozen month. East central France, towards the Rhine, has average temperatures of less than 35° F. in January, while the 40° line crosses the country from the Cotentin to the Causses and then swings east past the head of the Rhône delta. Only the extreme south-west and south-east have January temperatures higher than 42° F. While the Garonne basin as a whole is then warmer than the Rhône—a contrast to the summer conditions—the Riviera coast is distinct climatically with average temperatures up to 46° F. This winter warmth makes the Riviera a special region in many ways.

5 Climatic Regions

It is unprofitable, if not impossible, to lay down sharp lines on a map to separate distinct climatic regions. The climates of France are like her topographical features: they grade one into the other over wide transition zones. While there are many differences between Atlantic, Mediterranean and Continental provinces, there are also important divisions within these major provinces, corresponding in a general way to the arrangement of areas of high and low relief, with modifications due to aspect and exposure. The Mediterranean coast, the Paris basin and the Armorican peninsulas, for example, show certain climatic features which would justify us in describing them as climatic regions, but local variations, as between coast and interior in Brittany, may be very important. We shall consider some of these variations further in the regional descriptions, Part III.

Chapter 5

NATURAL VEGETATION AND CROPS

1 *Vegetation and Man*

The natural vegetation of any region of the world may be said
to provide a clue to the possibilities of human effort in that
region. It is controlled by the main physical facts such as location, elevation, exposure, soils and climate, and accordingly
summarizes these facts and offers a synthetic picture of the
environment. Man's activities are related in many ways to the
vegetation. In Europe he and his domesticated animals have,
in the course of centuries, brought about profound changes in
its character: they have, above all, waged war on forests and
reduced them to scattered fragments. This is especially true
of the richer agricultural areas like the Paris basin.

In the clearings thus formed man introduced food-crops and
fruit-trees where soil and climate were suitable. Marshes, too,
have been drained (as in the Dombes) and shifting sands (in
the Landes) clothed with trees. The whole face of nature,
except in the most inaccessible or useless parts, has been
changed by human activity, direct or indirect. But this change
has not always been to man's ultimate gain. In the Mediterranean lands, and in the high limestone zones of the Central
Plateau and the Pyrenees, forest-destruction has in places
turned the landscape into a barren waste. Once destroyed, the
vegetation of these dry areas is difficult to replace, and the
surface soil, often on steep slopes, is washed away. The conse-
quences may be disastrous.

But the French peasant normally makes full use of the woodlands and trees that have been spared. The hedgerow trees
are persistently lopped to supply firewood and small construc-
tional timber, and the graceful woods which the traveller sees
from the train are treated as a harvest and ruthlessly felled
every thirty or forty years. A wide range of minor industries—

tanning, cooperage, charcoal-burning, furniture-making, the manufacture of sabots and toys—depends on them. On the fruit of chestnut and beech man and his stock are nourished, while the leaves of the ash delight the cattle when grass fails. The value of reafforestation was advocated a century ago as a check to torrential erosion; it is now generally accepted, though the two world wars took a heavy toll of French forests. In parts of Haute Savoie a brave attempt has been made to redevelop the forest covering from the foot of the hills step by step upwards.

2 *The Forest*

It is calculated that about 20 per cent of the surface of the country is forested. While this figure is much higher than the English figure of 5 per cent, it is considerably lower than the German percentage of 27; and it is towards the German frontier, where the wooded Vosges look out towards the Black Forest ("Forest" here being synonymous with upland), that many of the remaining large woodlands of France are found. If we except the driest parts of the Mediterranean coast, the more exposed sections of the Atlantic coast, the highest plateaux and mountains, and certain areas of limestone, loose sand and marsh, it is probable that the whole country would, if left to nature, be forest-covered. The bulk of it would be of the deciduous type (oak, ash, beech, hazel, poplar, hornbeam, etc.), occurring sometimes as high forest, sometimes as dense thickets with close undergrowth often broken by swamp, or again thinning out into parkland in areas of dry subsoil.

Such forests spread over most of Europe long ago as the present-day humid climates became established. They were preceded by coniferous forests (pine and spruce) that have now retreated to the far north and are found in Scandinavia. In places, however, the coniferous trees kept their hold, and we find them today most typically in the Vosges, the Jura, the Alps and the Pyrenees. Higher still, under the snows, in the rich grasslands that give their name to the Alps, in the pastures of the Pyrenees (Celtic *Biren*, "High Pastures") and the Auvergne, and in the open summits of the Vosges that

kept their wild horses until a few centuries ago and still have
wolves, we may see relics of the old glacial steppe that once
lay open from the Atlantic to the plains of western Asia. The
loams of Alsace, Picardy and Beauce were probably never as
densely forested as the areas of heavy clay, but centuries of
agriculture have so altered their natural vegetation that it is
difficult to say what it originally was.

3 The Midi

Deciduous forests cannot withstand the climate of the Mediterranean lowlands, where the prolonged summer drought makes
it necessary for the vegetation to have some protection from
the sun's rays. Here evergreen trees and shrubs, often with
long roots to penetrate deep into the subsoil, are at home; and
this "Mediterranean" vegetation, which includes the olive,
myrtle, oleander, cypress, stone pine and the evergreen oak,
provides us with a useful guide to the distribution of the full
Mediterranean climate and civilization. The olive in particular, with its characteristic twisted trunk and grey hairy leaves,
is a very interesting index of the Mediterranean. Its fruit ripens
slowly and needs the long warm autumns occasioned by the
slow cooling of the surface waters of that sea. It disappears
in the west about Carcassonne, which thus guards a vegetational
frontier as well as a famous gate; and in the lower Rhône it
hardly reaches Valence, where the narrow corridor begins.
"À Valence", runs a local saying, "le Midi commence."

But some species of deciduous trees such as the beech survive where elevation brings more rain and lower temperatures,
and where man and beast have spared them, in the Mediterranean hills. The sweet chestnut, a valuable source of food,
is found in many parts of the Apennines, in Sicily and in
Corsica. In France it forms dense woods in the southern Alps,
but especially in the Chaîne des Maures. Here impermeable
rocks give rise to a very distinctive countryside.

The Riviera, with its winter warmth and shelter, will grow
the orange, and man has brought in a great variety of exotic
trees and shrubs, such as palms, acacias, the eucalyptus and
the prickly pear, to give many parts of this coast an almost

tropical scenery. A very useful tree of the south is the cork oak, which, with the pine and chestnut forests of the Maures, makes the department of Var one of the most densely wooded areas in the country.

In southern France, as in most parts of the Mediterranean, the ease with which introduced species establish themselves is remarkable and significant. Forest destruction does not extend grassland, but brings bush and scrub (*maquis*) in its wake, and leaves open spaces that can be colonized by alien plants. Cultivation, house-building, boat-building and the need of winter fuel have all contributed to the limitation of native tree-growth. Very harmful, too, are the leaf-picking activities of the goat, the animal best fitted to Mediterranean conditions.

In an area so well defined by nature as this, man's utilization of his environment has taken highly characteristic forms. The intensiveness of cultivation and the prolongation of the productive period even through the winter, compensate for the limitation of fertile areas. Moreover, from high antiquity, the upland pastures have been used in summer for stock rearing, for they are green and fresh when the lowlands are brown and burnt. This migratory movement of stock (or *transhumance*) is most typical of the deltaic lowlands of the Rhône: enormous flocks of sheep leave Crau and Camargue (nowadays travelling by rail, but formerly on foot) for the high pastures of Savoy and Dauphiny.

In the Mediterranean as a whole, the growing of fruit is a natural response to environmental conditions. We have hinted above at the importance of the olive in south France, and we must also mention the almond. With intensive cultivation, specialization is a strong feature: here it will suffice to notice the perfume industry of the Côte d'Azur in the Maritime Alps, which makes use of the scented shrubs native to the Mediterranean, and turns the orange-blossom into eau-de-Cologne. Specialized flower-growing is a feature of many parts of this south-eastern coast. Another luxury-industry is connected with the cultivation of the mulberry tree, which dislikes moist conditions although it will stand a good deal of cold. It overlaps the olive in distribution but extends farther north. To the traveller going south its appearance is one of the first signs of the Midi. The silk industry, centred in Lyon, is partly supplied with raw material from silk-worms fed on mulberry leaves grown in Languedoc and Provence.

4 *The Vine*

But it is the cultivation of the vine, the queen of French harvests, that brings the country special fame. France is un-rivalled both for the amount and for the variety of her wines. The four departments of the south coast, between the Albères and the river Rhône, are by far the largest producers, with Hérault leading. The vines are grown in thick rows in open fields or on terraced slopes; and the wine obtained is most cheap *vin ordinaire* for home consumption. As we leave the Mediterranean we find the vine grown both in the Rhône and in the Garonne basins, whereas the olive does not penetrate into the latter and occurs only a short distance up the Rhône. Both these river basins produce high-grade wines along their north-western sides. Near the mouth of the Garonne, in the department of Gironde, the climate is still very sunny while there is more moisture to swell the grapes, and this is the home of the best Bordeaux wines. The most renowned Burgundy wines are produced under the hills of the Côte d'Or and Beaujolais, on well-drained calcareous slopes with a south-eastern aspect. While the vineyards are small and the quantity of wine relatively slight, the value is considerable.

The northern limit of the vine runs parallel to the Channel from the mouth of the Loire to the Ardennes. The vine must have strong and continuous sunshine in late summer and early autumn. It does not do well under humid conditions, but with a moderate rainfall its deep roots find moisture during prolonged drought. In the Paris basin, towards the limit of vine cultivation, local conditions are all-important, and except in specially favoured spots the wines are apt to be sour. Considerable care is necessary and only the warmest soils and sunniest slopes can be utilized.

With these selective factors many of the wines of the north are exceptionally valuable. Thus in Champagne, on and under the warm slopes of the Falaise de l'Ile de France, wine-cultivation actually reaches its northern limit. Chablis is produced on the south side of the Seine basin, while the chalk slopes of the Loire and its tributaries yield well-known vintages especially about Saumur. In the hill-country of Lorraine, only favoured spots with sunny garden patches have the vine, but in Alsace, on loess terraces above the cold floor of the Rift Valley, it comes into its own again, though the quality of the wines quickly deteriorates towards the north.

In the wetter north-west of France apple-growing for cider largely replaces the vine, and in the north-east much beer is drunk. Among other fruit-bearing trees the sweet-chestnut has been mentioned above. It is abundant on the crystalline exposures of the Central Plateau, and provides an important accessory article of food in many hill districts south of latitude 46°. The walnut, valuable for the oil of its nuts, is most abundant along the Alpine tributaries of the Rhône and on the western slopes of the Plateau, but it is giving way rapidly to orchard trees. In many parts of the south these have been cultivated for centuries (we may instance the prune industry of Agen on the Garonne) but there is an increasing interest in dessert fruit —pears, apples, apricots, and particularly peaches.

5 *Cereal Crops*

Perhaps the oldest and most permanent fact about French agriculture is the importance of the wheat crop. Wheaten bread is almost everywhere eaten, and the white bread of France has often been contrasted with the black bread of Germany. The Paris basin has long been a famous cornland. It has fertile loams and well-mixed alluvial soils. Climatically its cool wet winters, prolonged springs and sunny summers are ideal, and this fact has encouraged the growth of wheat, with the aid of artificial fertilizers, even on the less suitable soils in the north. Beauce and Brie, Picardy and Artois are the best wheatlands; towards the north-west production diminishes rapidly, but wheat is extensively grown on the loams of Côtes-du-Nord in Brittany, in favoured rain-shadow areas.

Southwards, the crop remains important from the middle

Loire to the Garonne, where it is rivalled by maize in the wetter south-west. It is found throughout the Rhône-Saône basin and is the chief cereal grown in the Mediterranean districts, where there is, however, little room for cereal cultivation. While wheat is absent from the bleak poorer soils of the Central

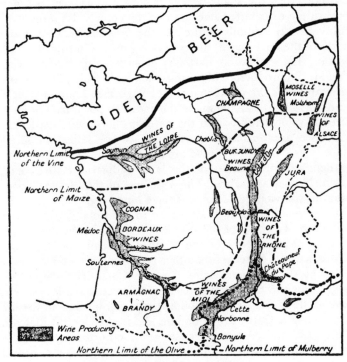

Figure 9 Some crops of France

Plateau, it is the main crop of the sheltered basins sunk into its northern edge, especially of the Limagne. This is true also of Alsace.

Rye and buckwheat are characteristic of the poorer cultivable parts of the Central Plateau and Brittany, while oats belong to the north and north-west. Barley is cultivated in the north from Brittany to Alsace, where it goes largely to the breweries. Maize is grown widely where hot summers are accompanied by a fair amount of rain—i.e., in the south-west and in the Saône basin.

6 *Other Crops*

Of root crops the sugar-beet is of first importance, but it is not widely distributed like most of the cereals. Its large-scale cultivation is virtually limited to the *limon* of the centre and north of the Paris basin, the crop being grown in rotation with wheat. An occupation that has extended rapidly in recent times is the production of *primeurs*, i.e., early fruits, flowers and vegetables for the great markets of Paris and London. Rapid transport facilities have made this industry possible. The sheltered bays of Brittany and the natural "hot-house" valleys of Provence are outstanding examples of specialization along these lines. More widespread are the areas of intensive market-gardening around most of the large industrial centres, e.g., Lyon, Nantes and Paris. The *hortillons*[1] of the Somme floodplain in the vicinity of Amiens have long been famous.

Reference has been made above to the upland pastures of the south. To those of the Alps we should add the grasslands of the volcanic rocks of the Central Plateau and the high pastures of the Pyrenees. Another type of grazing land is provided by the salt marshes of, e.g., the Cotentin, favoured by sheep. But the high wetter parts of the west have few sheep; here cattle thrive, and take on a special significance in the life of the people. Cattle are abundant also in the Central Plateau, the central and western Pyrenees and the northern rim of the Paris basin. Only in the lowlands of the Midi, where natural pastures are very scarce, do we find cattle replaced by goats as milk-producers. But cattle also provide power for ploughing and draught purposes in many parts of France.

Finally, it is fitting to mention here that harvest of the sea which France's long coast-line gives her. The Breton people have naturally made most use of these resources, and they still

---

[1] This word is applied in Picardy to marshy areas intersected by small canals and utilized, with the aid of heavy manuring, for the production of fruit and vegetables. (Latin *hortus* = garden.)

undertake long fishing expeditions in addition to their constant exploitation of the adjacent seas. The Bay of Biscay is famed for its oyster fisheries, while in the Mediterranean the sardine (which gets its name from Sardinia), the tunny and the anchovy are the usual catches.

PART II

THE HUMAN BACKGROUND

Chapter 6

THE PREHISTORIC BACKGROUND: RACIAL TYPES

1 *The Ice Age and Man*

Certain parts of the pleasant land of France have probably been continuously occupied from a very remote past, and we must now trace the main steps in the long process of adjustment between man and his environment. In doing this we must bear in mind that there have been changes in that environment as well as in man and his cultures. Nature appears fixed to our senses, but over long periods of time vital changes may take place: grassland may give way to desert or forest deteriorate to bogland, and man must inevitably change his habits or move on.

We catch our first glimpse of man in Europe during the Ice Age, when certain areas of the northern hemisphere were invaded by ice sheets which have left lasting traces in so many parts of our continent. It is generally held that there were four main advances of the ice, and between them three relatively mild "interglacial" stages. During these intervals of milder climate, each of them many thousands of years long, we can trace the movement into France of groups of people coming from North Africa. They lived by hunting wild animals such as the reindeer and the mammoth, and they were entirely ignorant of cultivation. In their wanderings they advanced northwards into Britain, which was still a part of the continent, and occupied southern England; eastwards they reached the neighbourhood of the Rhine valley. Beyond the Rhine, in central Europe, a rather different culture existed, marked by other kinds or fashions of tools, and from time to time this eastern culture spread westwards into what is now France.

2 The Hunter-Artists and their Decline

At last the final retreat of the ice set in, and as Europe slowly recovered from its effects, wide grassy steppes replaced the cold tundra. The "Old Stone Age" inhabitants of Europe had good hunting of the hoofed animals, e.g., wild horses and cattle, that lived on the grasslands. Several varieties of culture can be distinguished among these ancient hunters, and it is worth noting that many of the names by which prehistorians distinguish them have been taken from different parts of France where remains have been found.[1] Throughout this long period of time the south-western parts of France stand out prominently among the frequented regions of Europe. Movement and contact went on steadily along the hill-margins, and the limestone belts of the Central Plateau and the Pyrenees, with their natural caves, were occupied continuously for thousands of years. The Dordogne, in particular, is rich in remains of ancient man, and even the modern population bears traces of direct descent from far prehistoric man. The poor soils of the Dordogne are a great disadvantage nowadays, and it has become a region of poverty and of survival of ancient things.

Some of these prehistoric peoples made engravings and drawings, often skilfully executed and painted, on the walls of their caves. To them the name "hunter-artists" has been given. It seems that they practised their art with magical purpose—to bring luck in the chase—and most of the pictures are of animals and hunting scenes. As a rule the hunters lavished great care on their weapons and tools which were made of flint and bone.

But a decline set in. With the next change of environment, western Europe became the land of forests that it would still be if the hand of man were removed. When the ice-sheets finally melted (leaving, however, relics still in Scandinavia and the Alps), the westerly winds, previously shouldered out by the cold air, found their way into Europe north of the mountain-

---

[1] For example, *Aurignacian*, from Aurignac, in the Pyrenean foothills; *Solutrean*, from Solutré, near Mâcon, on the Saône.

belt. With them came that influence of the sea that has meant so much in the story of Europe. Warm rains brought forests in their wake, forests first of pine, as we have seen, and then of oak, ash and thorn, and dense undergrowth spread wherever the soils permitted.

The herds of docile hoofed animals no longer had grassy plains to roam over; they were forced to retreat, and man's food supply was sadly diminished. The old active hunting life deteriorated: man was as yet unable to fight the forest—he feared it for the dangerous animals it sheltered—and he became more and more a mere collector, living on roots, nuts, berries and sea-shells along seashores and rivers and in scattered areas not densely forested.

3 *Mediterranean Man*

After another long period of time the climate warmed considerably and the rainfall decreased, and new activities which will be described in Chapter 7 brought a re-awakening along new lines. Agriculture and trade were developed in western Europe, and peoples from the western Mediterranean region spread northwards as farmers and herders. It is from these peoples, mingling to some extent with earlier stocks, that the present general population of south-western Europe has evolved. To it the name Mediterranean race is sometimes given.

The dry limestone belts of Aquitaine retained something of their old importance, and formed natural avenues prolonging the way around the eastern Pyrenees, leading to the Atlantic coasts of Europe. Here the Mediterranean race remains an important element in the modern inhabitants of several regions, including the British Isles.

The stocks included under the name "Mediterranean" are usually rather short in stature and slight in build; the face is normally oval, the head-shape long, the hair and eyes dark and the skin rather darker than in other European types, grading to a light olive-brown in the extreme south. This stock has taken kindly to life in cities, and it has given southern France a human link with many other Mediterranean coastlands.

4 *Alpine Man*

Once more this northward movement of people was balanced in western Europe by a colonization of farmers from the east, markedly different in type and having affinities with the inhabitants of western Asia. These folk were broad-headed. Groups of them found their way west along the loess belts to Bavaria and to Belgium, Alsace and the Paris basin.

Their subsequent spread through the mountain belt of central Europe involved a long and stubborn fight with a difficult environment, and the struggle seems to have stamped the race with a patient endurance and a capacity for conscientious industry that remain characteristic. Peasant agriculture and handicrafts have been its traditional occupations. Because of the early association of this race-type with the mountain areas it has been given the somewhat misleading name of "Alpine".

In build these European broad-heads are rather short and thick-set; their colouring is neither dark nor fair, but something between the European extremes, and the skin is often inclined to be thick.

Guided west by the mountain lines that link France with central Europe, people of this type came to occupy the Central Plateau and advanced thence to the Pyrenees and to the Armorican peninsula. Thus they have long formed a considerable constituent of the French population, and they are especially important among the peasantry.

5 *Nordic Man*

The last of the three principal races of Europe is also fairly well represented in France. The name "Nordic" is commonly applied to this stock, but this label, and the even more misleading term "Aryan", should perhaps be forgotten because of the emotions they arouse.

Its ancestry has been traced back to a branch of the ancient hunters who lived on the Russian steppe: it came west at various times along the loess belt and it has taken a lead in "hunting and shooting" and in organization from the very dawn of civilization in Europe. The leaders of the Celtic migrations that took place in the early days of iron seem to have belonged to this race, and the post-Roman invaders of France probably included many of this type.

Members of this race may be recognized by their tall stature, big bones and muscles, their blond hair and blue or grey eyes. The head-shape is long. From the early days of metal, at least, there has been intermixture between this race and the Alpine type described above, and many populations of the plains adjoining the central European mountains show the head-breadth of the Alpine race combined with the stature and the fair colouring of the Nordic.

Similar intermixture has occurred between the other racial stocks, especially in the river basins where people have been increasingly thrown together; and such mixing has perhaps been commonest in that melting-pot of western Europe, the Paris basin. But in fact the French region as a whole tended from very early times to be the meeting-place of various peoples and their cultures. The Old Stone Age cultures derived from the east normally found their westward limit near the Pyrenees, while those of southern origin commonly advanced to about the Rhine. Thus the area where overlapping took place is approximately that known to history as France. This helps us to understand the permanence of the influence exerted on man by the broad facts of physical geography.

Chapter 7

THE DAWN OF CIVILIZATION

1 *The Beginnings*

In the ancient world, as in the world today, no region could progress unless it came into contact with other regions. This factor of communication or intercourse has been highly important in the history of civilization, and we have suggested how the variety of contacts in France has contributed to that country's special place in European civilization. But for many millennia before our era France was merely part of the forested fringe of the great land-mass of Eurasia, the end of a complicated peninsular region (Europe) thrust out into the misty northern seas and remote from the open steppes, the inland seas and great rivers where man first advanced from savagery to civilization.

In south-western Asia, between the Nile on the west and the Indus on the east, man had learnt to domesticate nature from a very early date, and by 7000 B.C. cereal cultivation (dependent on the domestication of wild grasses) and the keeping of tamed animals for use were known in that region. This is not the place to trace the steps in those immensely important discoveries, but we should notice that they permitted or even necessitated permanent settlement—the fixing of human societies to their homeland—and allowed the accumulation of tradition and, to some extent, of material wealth. A society which lives by hunting must be constantly on the move and cannot accumulate much property. The production of food is in fact a very different thing from the collecting and hunting of wild resources, and with it came many new ideas and a changed mental outlook. Food-production also meant improved diet and could support much larger populations.

But none of the civilized arts and crafts which the agriculturists evolved, and which included means of communication

by sea, reached Europe much before 4000 B.C. Most of the
north-west remained untouched until a later date, its peoples
clustering on wind-swept shores and living mainly by hunting
and fishing.

2 *The Spread of Civilization*

Gradually, however, groups of grain-growers spread through
Asia Minor and reached the islands of the Aegean Sea and the
lower basin of the Danube. The native food-collectors of the
fertile loess regions were slowly converted to the arts of cultivation, and a civilization to which the name Danubian has
been given grew up in east central Europe. The old life in time
disappeared and the neolithic (or *new stone*) culture took its
place.

This gets its name from the fact that the former dependence
on stones of a kind that could be chipped, like flint, was broken
down, and stones of many varieties came to be used, stones
that could be ground and polished to the desired shape,
whether for hoe or axe or wedge. In reality, however, the
change that was taking place was much greater than this
change from one kind of stone to another; it was the evolution
from barbarism to civilization, though the civilized arts of
writing and building in stone were still unknown in central
Europe.

From the Danube, growing crops in patches of cleared
forest, these cultivating peasants moved north-westwards during the third millennium B.C. It has been shown that the
advance was made along the light loess soils, rich and easily
cultivated, strung out between the basin of Hungary and the
north of France (see Fig. 10). At the end of this long line of
movement lay the Paris basin, and long before 2000 B.C. small
settlements were being made here in forest clearings, not far
from the great city that has focused the life of the region in the
historic period.

But there are more ways than one into western Europe. Along
the northern foot of the Alps the peasants had established
themselves in houses raised on piles by the shores of lakes that
the glaciers had left behind them. From Lake Geneva and the

Jura they crossed the valley of the Saône and reached Burgundy and the Central Plateau.

The ways along the rivers and by the hills are thus accounted for: there remains to be considered the way of the sea. By this time there had grown up flourishing trading cities on favourable sites in the Aegean area, whither the knowledge of copper and gold had spread from nearer Asia. These cities, anxious to obtain supplies of metal, traded with the coasts to the west,

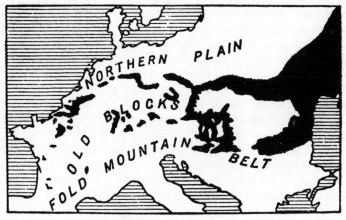

Figure 10 Loess Soils

and *via* Sicily, the half-way-house of the Mediterranean, elements of civilization trickled through to the south coast of France.

Before the end of the fourth millennium the new era dawned on the edge of the Atlantic, coming to Brittany by way of Portugal and by land across the isthmus of Aquitaine, and France was invaded on all sides by ideas originating in the ancient East. Archaeological discoveries and researches enable us to trace the penetration of these new ideas northward from the Mediterranean along the twin avenues that nature has placed east and west of the Central Plateau. By the Gate of Carcassonne and along the limestone exposures, the custom spread of erecting great stone "megaliths" over the dead, and a knowledge of grain and of pottery was diffused through western and north-western France.

About 2000 B.C. pottery of a distinctive type, known as beaker-pottery, came into fashion in central Europe and in Spain. It is not clear in which region it originated, but it is important for our purpose to note that France was the connecting link between these two regions. We find the two civilizations, that of central Europe and that of the sea coasts, coming into contact and mingling in parts of France, and especially in the south-east and the north-west. Both Provence and Brittany have a very ancient background of maritime activity, and we may note the fame of Marseille and Toulon, of Brest and Lorient, in the modern world.

3 *The Bronze Age*

By this time, well before 2000 B.C., the people of the near East had made the important discovery that the addition of tin to copper produced an alloy, bronze, which made cutting tools much harder and more serviceable than any previously known. With this, the Bronze Age made its appearance: the new metal came to be used for all kinds of tools and weapons, and a knowledge of bronze was extended along the two ways, the Danubian and the Mediterranean, from the Aegean. By sea, bronze axes and daggers were carried to many of the coasts of western Europe. Those parts which had copper, gold or tin came into prominence and in France it was Brittany, with its tin and its precious stones, that became the chief centre of activities.

At about the same period a knowledge of bronze, passing up the Danube, had reached Bohemia which, like Brittany, is a shattered remnant of the Hercynian mountains, once rich in surface supplies of both tin and gold. From Bohemia the knowledge of metals was carried westwards into north-east France, enriching the neolithic cultures that had been introduced there long before.

In western Europe the manufacture of bronze implements thus arose in certain localities where metals were available, and an active trade was maintained between those culture-centres. We know a good deal, thanks to the great work of

Déchelette, about the cultures of France in the early Metal Age. The French Atlantic coast stands out clearly as an important trade centre linked with the Iberian peninsula. Around the western Alps, a metal culture of central European origins grew out of the neolithic civilization which had come along the foothill lake-route. It traded with Spain by way of south France.

France was far from being a cultural unit at this remote time, but thanks to her position and to the ways of communication that meet and cross in this part of Europe, the two cultures, that of the Atlantic and that of the Danube valley, were gradually mingling with each other and being enriched by Mediterranean contacts. In Brittany, which is the end of the land-mass and the natural meeting-place of coastal routes, a great expansion and specialization in the building of great stone monuments took place in the early Metal Age. These monuments of Morbihan are among the most remarkable relics of their kind in the world. Reverence for their sanctity is still a feature of Breton life, and folk-ritual is full of practices connected with them.

As the Bronze Age advanced through the second millennium, improved methods of casting and new types of tools enabled man to enlarge his tiny clearings in the forests that still hemmed him in on all sides. In this effort he was aided by a period of warm and rather dry climate, when forest clearance by burning seems to have been practised in Europe north of the fold mountains. Thus the areas of settlement were enlarged. Numerous sickles of bronze which have been found in south-eastern France bear witness to the extension of cultivation. The lower Seine valley now stands out strongly as a region of settlement trading with Britain. Here we have the first indication of the subsequent historic concentration of maritime life in the coastal province of Normandy.

The late Bronze Age witnessed the relative decline of the old way of the sea and the entry into France from central Europe of new forces which bring us into close touch with the historic scene. Chief among the introductions were the domesticated horse and the sword. Long-distance trade developed and the powers of movement and of conquest were enlarged. Such changes brought a stratification of society. Cultivating peasant communities governed by men who possessed horses were organized in western Europe, but none of these village settlements grew to anything like the size or significance of the cities of the Mediterranean. Craftsmanship and tradition ac-

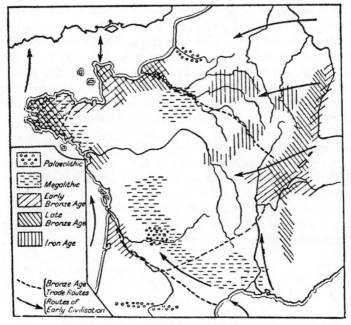

Figure 11 Some Prehistoric Culture-areas

cumulated, however, though the use of bronze slowly declined following the introduction, not long after 1000 B.C., of a knowledge of weapons of iron.

4 *The Iron Age*

The men of the iron sword were probably pastoral folk from beyond the Rhine who spread across France by way of the Jura, Burgundy, and the limestone girdle of the Central

Plateau. By 500 B.C. some of them had crossed the Pyrenees into Spain, just as did the barbarians who invaded the Roman Empire a thousand years later. These iron-users settled near salt-supplies; they probably needed salt for making butter and preserving meat and for eating with cereals. With their hard axes they could enlarge the forest clearings and cut ways through the woods.

For much of Europe the early Iron Age was a time of great unrest. There is some evidence that the climate was somewhat colder and wetter than it is at present, and unsettled conditions constantly forced groups of people to wander. Some of the migrants who moved into France from beyond the Rhine brought with them the Celtic languages that Caesar found there and which are now spoken only in the outer fringes of western Europe. Later on, the building of great fortresses hints that military rule and warfare were common features of life in western Europe.

A second stage of the early Iron Age, named after La Tène in Switzerland, had come into being by 500 B.C. and is well represented in Champagne. The origin and significance at the La Tène culture, with its characteristic styles of decorative art, are related to the renewed activity of the Mediterranean culture-stream. We must now turn our attention to the south.

Chapter 8

ROMAN AND GOTHIC FRANCE

1 *The Greek Colonies*

In the eastern Mediterranean there came a fresh expansion of life during the last millennium B.C., which culminated in the classical civilization seen at its best in 5th-century Athens. It has been suggested that this blossoming of culture was based on the material prosperity of a period when more moisture was available for agriculture. A phase of cool damp climate, for which there is evidence in Northern Europe from about 750 B.C., would mean a good deal in increased rain to a rather dry region such as the Mediterranean. City-life, long enriched by the cultivation of the olive, brought to that area wealth and leisure that gave opportunity for discussion and for artistic and literary achievement.

The Aegean archipelago offered unique facilities for maritime trade. The Greek cities, like the earlier cities of that region, profited by this trade, and to promote it they planted daughter-cities or colonies around many of the Mediterranean coasts. When, about 600 B.C., they had reached the north coast of the western Mediterranean and founded the city of *Massalia* (Marseille) under the hills at the entrance to the Rhône valley, a new chapter was opened in the story of the land that was to become France.

The colonists seem to have introduced the cultivation of the vine. They had olive-groves and carried on an extensive export trade in olive oil. From the adjacent sea they obtained fish and coral. Trade with the interior involved the penetration of the Rhône corridor: wine and coral were exchanged for the products of the north (salted meat, tin and pitch) and the infiltration of the civilized arts of Greece and Etruscan Italy transformed the native Iron Age into the La Tène culture referred to in Chapter 7.

Leaving the Saône where the river turns at Châlon, and where the railway north leaves it today, a trade route led over the Côte d'Or into the Paris basin. Here, in Champagne, a special development of La Tène culture was centred. It is interesting to compare this with the mediaeval fame of Champagne, when great fairs were held in this region of transit and exchange, placed where the Rhône-Saône trade current reached the gathered ways of the north.

There were other Greek colonies on the south coast besides Massalia, e.g., Antipolis (Antibes), Nicaea (Nice), and Agatha (Agde), and there was close settlement up the Rhône as far as Avignon.

Some penetration of Greek trade took place also along the Garonne valley, but from now on the Rhône gateway was to take more and more of the traffic between south and north: the older way was sidetracked and so preserved an older life. The Garonne Valley, opening to the Atlantic, has tended to have contacts with the ocean while the gate of the Rhône was in closer connection with the Mediterranean world.

2 The Coming of Rome

It was from Italy, with the Roman conquest, that the next external influence came to France. Rome began in some ways as an ordinary city state, but she enlarged the current conception of citizenship and so made a great contribution to the political experience of the world. Through Massalia Rome came into contact with south France, and by the end of the second century B.C. she had established the province of Gallia Narbonensis. This *Provincia Romana*, whence the name Provence, became the essentially Roman part of France, and the relation between its boundaries and those of the "Mediterranean" region is worthy of study.

The actual limits of the province included Toulouse and Vienne, strategic points where routes were concentrated before entering the restricted passages of Carcassonne and Valence. But the area of effective colonization was limited to the region which grows the olive, i.e., with environmental conditions recalling those of the Roman homeland. Here cities were founded which enjoyed the full civic life of the Mediterranean. Their public buildings often survive to bear testimony to the high civilization and to the architectural skill of Rome—the great amphitheatres of Nîmes and Arles, the Maison Carrée at Nîmes, the Pont du Gard, the theatre at Orange. Roman place-names are common (see Pl. II).

Beyond the limits of the Roman province Gaul, at the time of Caesar, was said to be "divided into three parts". The largest division, *Celtica*, stretched from the Alps over the Central Plateau and the southern half of the Paris basin to Brittany. North of the lower Seine, and north and east of the Marne, lay *Belgica*, its southern boundary following here and there the forested clay belts under the scarps of the Paris basin, and its eastern limit running along the Rhine. In the south-west, beyond the Garonne for the most part, was *Aquitania*: the Basque tongue which has survived in the western Pyrenees is held to have been the language spoken by the Aquitanians. Celtic languages were spoken by Caesar's Celts and Belgae.

By advancing north and west from the Roman province, Caesar was able to bring the whole of Gaul into the Empire, and its romanization followed through four centuries of Roman rule. Among all the achievements of Rome, it has been said, the romanization of western Europe was the greatest.

3 Cities and Roads

With the Romans, the idea of the city penetrated for the first time into Europe north of the mountain belt. South-west France, with its genial climate and its wine and wheat, came to have a fair measure of romanization, but north of about the 46th parallel the organization was on a more military basis; and ever since there have been certain differences between the parts of France roughly north and south of this line. They were reflected in the division into occupied and unoccupied France (1940–45).

As a rule the cities of the north grew out of Roman camps placed at crossings of roads and rivers. The native peoples came to settle in these towns, and they adopted the Latin tongue.

Some of these settlements have probably been occupied without a break ever since, but most of them were deserted in the dark ages to revive later on. In the west, Brittany, with its damp climate and maritime activities, was not effectively

Figure 12 Roman Roads

Romanized, but along the eastern frontier intensive military occupation took place. From Cologne (Colonia Agrippina) to Basel a famous string of frontier stations was established, all on or near the left bank of the Rhine. Of these Strasbourg alone is now French.

Besides towns and cities, there came to western Europe at this time the first made roads, "Rome n'a pas frayé les voies; elle les a seulement pavées," [1] and it is true that in following certain lines laid down by nature she followed ways of movement that had been used for long ages before her. But the Roman roads were not only paved: they were systematized and organized into a comprehensive and coherent network.

The main connecting link between north and south followed the left bank of the Rhône up to Lyon, as main road and railway do today, and thence the right bank of the Saône to Châlon. In the Paris basin, roads followed the Seine and the Loire to reach the sea. The Garonne also had its road, leading from Narbonne through Toulouse to Bordeaux. Thus the main river-lines stand out clearly.

In the north, the area between the Seine, Rhine and Scheldt (approximately Caesar's Belgica) was distinguished by the closeness of its network, and Durocortorum (Reims) was a road centre of outstanding importance. It lies in the dry Champagne on the line which continues the "pointer" of the Rhône northwards: across the low limestone plateaux of the north the Romans drove their straight roads with ease.

The roads of Gaul may be said to have shaped the destinies of France. They illustrate the Roman genius for practical achievement since they provided an enduring frame for the function that France was fitted by nature to perform—that of mediator between the Mediterranean and the Ocean. For centuries after the power of Rome had collapsed, her roads remained to astonish the invaders, to serve as military and commercial highways and, above all, to focus anew the life of the countryside in fairs and market towns.

Besides her cities and connecting roads, Rome left in France many cultural elements of permanent importance—her language, her engineering skill, the spirit of liberalism and toleration, the ideal of universalism and, not least, the majesty of her name. She left Christianity and Christian bishops in many cities which were to live through the Dark Ages.

---

[1] "Rome did not blaze the trails, she merely paved them."

4 *The Barbarians*

The later Roman period witnessed the renewal and in time the dominance of the Central European stream in France. Barbarian tribes poured against the Roman frontier and in the 5th century established themselves in nearly every part of France. Chief among the invaders were groups known as the Vandals, Goths, Franks, Alamans and Burgundians. They advanced along the lowland routes between the Alps and the North Sea, through Flanders, up the Moselle and by the Gate of Belfort. For the most part the surplus population of central Europe, they spoke Germanic dialects, and their leaders, at any rate, were of Nordic stock. Of these various groups the Franks, who had swept along the northern plain from the region between the Rhine and the Weser, were destined to have the greatest influence on later history. In the hill country to the south, penetration was not so easy, but the Burgundians, coming through the Gate of Belfort, gained possession of the Rhône-Saône valley and for a time occupied the Mediterranean coastlands.

The rough powerful Franks, under Clovis, became the dominant group before the end of the 5th century, and they gradually conquered all Gaul with the significant exceptions of Brittany (into which Celtic-speaking immigrants came over from southwest Britain when the Anglo-Saxons invaded England), and the Mediterranean coast between the Pyrenees and the Rhône delta, which long remained an extension of Visigothic Spain.

But though the Roman civilization was submerged, the Christian church became the heir to the Roman tradition. Clovis, who had married a Christian princess, was baptized in 496, and soon all France became Christian, though many pagan customs survived often in Christianized forms.

5 *Rural Settlements*

The Frankish element was strongest between the Loire and the Rhine, and it was to this northern part of Gaul that the name France came specially to apply. As rude warriors and men of the sword they were unskilled in civic organization, but became overlords of village-settlements in which the Gallo-Roman people clustered together, and from them the Franks learned the language which has become French.

North of the Loire, the basic unit of society came to be the compact village with its fields cultivated in common by peasants under the protection of an overlord. It is possible or even probable that the germ of this system is pre-Frankish and pre-Roman, but it is in any case true that this peasant society became a widespread feature of northern Europe during the centuries that followed the barbarian invasions.

In Brittany and other parts of the west, however, though there are some exceptions, a different social system appears, with family farms instead of compact villages, giving that part of France a distinctive life and a distinctive landscape still. South of the Loire only a few districts had the common-field system, and south of about lat. 46° the civil life of Roman Gaul survived to a great extent, while in the extreme south-west the Basque type of settlement, as evidenced by the distribution of the Basque house, extended much beyond the present limits of that language.

In the 8th century a new invader appeared in western Europe—the Moor. France was now assailed from the south, along the "African avenue" under the eastern Pyrenees. This lowland route coming from the south through the Gate of Poitou reached the Loire at Tours, and here the invaders were scattered by Charles Martel in 732. France was thus saved from being dominated by Islam, but the old Mediterranean trade routes were cut off for a time,[1] and Christendom awaited the lead of Charlemagne.

[1] Many parts of the Mediterranean coast were attacked by sea and the trade of the old Roman ports was interrupted. The invaders established a footing in the wooded hills of the Chaine des *Maures*, where it is possible that their name (English *Moors*) survives. The word may refer, however, to the dark colouring of the woods.

Chapter 9

THE EXPANSION OF THE NORTH

1 *Charlemagne's Empire*

In northern France, while a village civilization was emerging from the turbulence of the barbarian invasions, a new organization, that of the Church, came into existence side by side with it. Some of the Roman cities lived through the crisis, as we have seen, especially those along the Rhine and in the Paris basin—among others Cologne, Coblenz, Mainz, Strasbourg, Rouen, Sens, Reims and Tours. The leaders of these cities were bishops who came to represent the heritage of law, order and culture from Roman days, and the memory of the world which Rome had unified haunted the popular mind.

By the year 800 Charlemagne had, in fact, restored for a time the unity and peace of Roman days. This great leader enlarged the territory of the Franks by extending it to include Central Europe, much of Italy, and a strip of Spain south of the Pyrenees, called the Spanish March. He also did much to revive learning, gathered scholars at Aix-la-Chapelle (Aachen) and collected books and manuscripts. Most of the manuscripts from which the texts of the printed classics are taken date from the age of Charlemagne. He evolved a system of administration and established a series of Marches, or border-states, to defend his frontiers. Later on his name was invested with a romantic glamour and he became an almost legendary figure in the annals of Christendom.

But his empire did not endure. Communications between its various parts were inadequate to maintain order, and it perished with its founder. It was out of the divisions of the empire that the great states of western Europe were to arise.

Three countries emerged from the Treaty of Verdun in 843 —France, or the land of the western Franks, Germany, and (between them) Lotharingia. The eastern frontier of this middle kingdom lay along the Rhine in Alsace and the Rhine gorge, the western ran from the mouth of the Rhône to the mouth of the Scheldt. The Lotharingian corridor thus consisted of a series of valleys running north and south: Rhône-Saône, Rhine, Meuse, Moselle and Scheldt. Through it ran important and ancient lines of communication, and at the northern end, where the hills faced the Great European Plain, lay Charlemagne's capital, Aix-la-Chapelle.

Figure 13 Charlemagne's Empire

The main function of this strip of country, which soon split up, was to be a transition or buffer zone between east and west. The barbarian invasions had carried Germanic speech west of the old Roman frontier, especially along the Moselle and the Plain of Flanders, so that the Romance and Germanic tongues met and still meet along an irregular boundary in this zone. Lotharingia leaves its name behind in Lorraine, which became a duchy of the "Holy Roman Empire", the ghostly successor of Charlemagne's domain.

In France also, subdivision followed the break-up of Charlemagne's empire. The feudal movement neutralized all efforts at centralization and resulted in the formation of local duchies, divided again into lordships, only very loosely dependent on the central authority. The seven great seigneuries were: the Duchy of France (around Paris), the Duchy of Brittany, the Counties of Toulouse and Flanders and the Duchies of Burgundy, Aquitaine (Guyenne) and Gascony. Other counties and duchies were carved out of the former Roman provinces in the 10th century.

2 The Capetian Kingdom

But before the end of the tenth century, in 987, a new political growth began with the accession of Hugh Capet. Charlemagne's conception of a revival of the Roman Empire survived east of the Rhine as the Holy Roman Empire; it was in the west that the new idea arose. The Duchy of France emerged to become before long the first kingdom of Europe which has had a continuous development into modern times. The house of Capet reigned unchallenged until the end of the 18th century.

What were the geographical factors in the early emergence of the Paris region? The royal territory included the counties of Paris, Melun, Orléans and Étampes, and above all the two nodal points of the northern river basins, Paris and Orléans. It stretched between these two cities, between the Seine and the Loire, and beyond these rivers to embrace the forested Sologne—a hunting ground—to the south, and a strip of fertile wooded country between the Oise and the Marne to the north.

It thus occupied the very heart of the Paris basin, a natural region traversed by a converging system of rivers that were coming to be used more and more for transport. The central area had been settled and farmed since Neolithic times. The land between the Seine and the Loire is the centre of the Tertiary limestone deposits, the last of the geological saucers of the basin, and midway between the two rivers is the broad expanse of fertile *limon* that makes the Beauce. This favoured heart of the basin is also the area of lowest rainfall, and, with its reasonably assured summer sun, it has long been famous for its crops, especially wheat. Around it in every direction lay lands less rich and more isolated (see Fig. 14).

The new growth therefore began in a region of good agriculture which was also the natural focal point of north France. The rise of regional consciousness was furthered by the revival of the old roads of Rome and of the bishops' cities placed where the roads came together.

3 *Cities and Market-Towns*

We have seen how these cities had taken over the heritage of Rome, its law and culture and universalism. In the 11th and 12th centuries, side by side with the political organization of the Capets, a great expansion of civic life took place, to continue through the Middle Ages. The towns that revived grew up in close connection with the peasantry round about. Small industries dependent on local sales made their appearance, and to the market-place the country-folk came to exchange their goods. The cathedral, usually overlooking the market-place and not in a "close" as in England, is still the dominating centre of these cities, as anyone knows who has visited Reims, Chartres or Amiens (see Pl. II). It was much more than a place of worship: the nave was used as a common hall, a court of justice and a market. Fairs, coming to be held under the protection of the church, often took place at first in the church. The association of fairs with Saints' days is a feature here as in England (e.g., St. Giles' Fair at Oxford).

Of the archbishoprics that of Sens stood out strongly in the Paris basin. The Roman city on the Yonne (Agedincum) was an important centre of routes. The road from the south passed through it in a direct line from the Saône valley to Paris and the lower Seine. So it became the gateway to the Paris region, and its great diocese remained until 1791 to show the power it had derived from its position.

In the Paris basin, then, the Roman cities took on a new life and became the cathedral cities and market-towns of the

Middle Ages. Here and there, too, a market-town grew up, usually on a river, where the Romans had not established a settlement. A scheme of life was evolved, with town and country, *bourgeois* (burgess) and peasant, closely linked together, a scheme that has survived with remarkable persistence, though naturally with modifications, down to the present day. Many of the features that distinguish French civilization can be traced to this long intimacy between urban and rural communities.

Paris itself, a village on its little island in Roman times, had become, by the 12th century, the finest capital in Europe, and on a hill to the south there gathered a celebrated University, attracting students from the ends of Christendom. The brilliant expansion of activity and thought in the Paris basin during the early Middle Ages may be illustrated by reference to the art of building construction. It was the central part of the Paris basin that witnessed the rise of the Gothic style of architecture from about 1150 onwards, and that produced cathedrals which are among the finest expressions of human effort and skill the world can show. It is worth noting that the easily-worked limestones so abundant in the area contributed not a little to their characteristic wealth of architectural detail.

The Gothic fashion spread widely from the Paris basin, and the directions of its diffusion clearly show the many contacts of northern France. Through the eastern gates it reached the Rhine and central Europe: Strasbourg has been called the extreme eastern home of pure Gothic architecture. By way of the Flanders Gap it spread to the north European Plain, where the style was converted into brick in the stoneless flats of the Low Countries. Northwards it penetrated into England by Canterbury in its "continental angle". It was carried along the historic avenue to the west of the Central Plateau, and reached Bordeaux and Bayonne, and Santander, Leon and Burgos in north Spain. It also travelled down the Saône basin towards the Mediterranean.

Yet there are very few successful Gothic buildings in the south of France. Narbonne and Montpellier have the style, it is true, but their cathedrals cannot compare with those of the north. On the other hand we find the Romanesque style (derived from the Roman) flourishing in this Roman part of France; and at Toulouse the fine brick church of St. Sernin is a nobler building than the Gothic cathedral.

4 *The South*

The architecture of the south is strongly regionalist. There were five centres or schools of Romanesque building, in Aquitaine, Auvergne, Languedoc, Provence and Burgundy. This fact may be used to demonstrate an important point in the story of France. It suggests regional virility but it reveals at the same time the general weakness of the south as compared with the north. Southern France lacked the unifying influence of a central river basin.

The lowlands south of the 46th parallel are divided into two clear sections by the southern part of the Central Plateau and the Montagne Noire. The western basin, cut off from the Mediterranean in climate and vegetation, is broad-based on the Atlantic and has had many contacts, first with Spain, then with the British Isles and later with the New World by the entry of the Gironde. It has no single dominating city. The truly Mediterranean lowlands are divided by the barrier of the Rhône into Languedoc and Provence: they too have no common centre. In addition there are three sharply isolated upland areas of the Pyrenees, the Central Plateau and the Alps.

Thus the southern half of France is a series of dissimilar regions which have found it difficult to act together. The legacy of Rome brought certain common features, it is true, but political unification was impossible, and the south lay open to domination by the organized power of the north.

Culturally, in addition to the Romanesque style of building, the following are features which have distinguished the south from the north. The Romance dialects that took shape there were nearer to the Latin than those of the north. They are known as the Langue d'Oc. Standard French, however, has grown out of the Langue d'Oil of the north. The boundary between these two forms of speech (approximately 46° N.) is similar to that which marks the northern limit of the part of France where Roman Law was revived and accepted from the 12th and 13th centuries onwards. This law (*droit écrit*) was maintained here until the French Revolution.

Moreover, Christianity took on rather different forms in the south: it often retained vestiges of older religions, while the habit of free discussion, perhaps a heritage from Rome, gave rise to the Albigensian[1] heresy and later on to the Huguenot revolt, both centred in the south and south-west. In many southern cities, we may remark, the church buildings have not the prominence they have in the north: the civic monuments of the Roman period often occupy the city centres. (Cf. Pl. II.)

5 *Political Expansion*

We are now in a position to understand how it came about that the political organization of the north gradually spread to the south, and we can briefly trace the steps in that expansion. At first the enlargement of the kingdom was confined to adjacent areas mainly within the basin. In the early 13th century it was greatly increased following the confiscation of the English possessions to the north-west.

This coastal province (Normandy) was based on the lower Seine, where the roving Northmen had settled in the 9th and 10th centuries. The wooded Seine in the *Vexin*, along the edge of the Tertiary clays, formed the frontier between it and the royal domain, with Château-Gaillard on the Norman side. French culture held a strong fascination for the Northmen, who absorbed it rapidly. Their "Norman" architecture (which is essentially Romanesque) testifies, in north France and in England, to the hold that Roman ideas had over them.

The eastern section of the Paris basin kept its independence longer, but with the acquisition of Champagne the kingdom extended to the Meuse. Of the chief regions of the north, only Lorraine and Brittany, always somewhat aloof, remained outside by the early 14th century.

Meanwhile parts of the south had revolted against the Roman church and gone over to the Albigensian heresy. Chris-

[1] "Men of Albi."

tian forces were organized and the Albigensian Crusade (1229) sent south. After a bitter struggle the centralized power of the north added to its political conquests almost the whole of Languedoc.

The areas east of the Rhône-Saône line, and Burgundy, were still outside the monarchy, while in the south-west the English kings were in possession and tried, in the long struggles of the Hundred Years War, to extend their territory and to

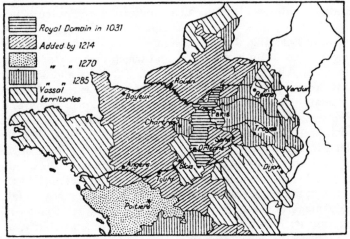

Figure 14 Mediaeval France: The Paris Basin (Historic)

become masters of France. This interlude came to an end in 1453, when England gave up all her French possessions except Calais. Part of the western Alps (Dauphiny) came in during the 14th century, but not until later in the 15th were the two seaward ends, Brittany and Provence, added to the French kingdom. At this time, too, Burgundy, the mightiest and richest of the feudal states, long distinct and secure in its possession of the important passes of the Côte d'Or, finally became part of the royal domain.

By the early 16th century, then, France as we know it had definitely taken shape, though Savoy and Alsace-Lorraine had still to come in.

Chapter 10

THE RENAISSANCE AND AFTER: MODERN FRANCE

1 *The Revival of Learning*

Side by side with the political unification of France a new spirit was winging its way through western Europe—the Revival of Learning. The Renaissance brought influences which have lasted to the present day and which contributed greatly to the making of the modern world. From the middle of the 15th century, under the inspiration, to some extent, of Greek scholars fleeing from the invasions of the Turk, the arts of life—painting, architecture, literature and politics—showed a rich and vigorous development. The cities of Italy took the lead in this new growth, and from Italy, as centuries before from Rome, the culture of the Mediterranean reached the French Midi and sped up the Rhône corridor to knock at the gates of the Paris basin. The French kings were ready to take advantage of the opportunities offered. They set about converting Paris into a court city, and the French nobility, attracted to the court, tended to become obedient subjects and were shorn of their power and independence.

A centralized nation-state thus emerged from a collection of feudal provinces. Burgundians and Bretons, Picards and Gascons, were beginning to call themselves Frenchmen. Culture, centralized at the court, took on definite national characteristics. In the 16th century, with the rise of printing, French replaced Latin as the language of the educated and in the 17th, "*le grand siècle*", it became the vehicle of a great classical literature. In architecture the Paris region and the Middle Loire, famous for its Renaissance buildings, had special prominence at this time.

Meanwhile, the new attitude of enquiry had produced a revolt against the power and doctrines of the Roman church in many parts of Europe, notably in Germany, Holland, Switzerland and England. In France it was especially the south that became Protestant and suffered the persecution of the Catholic crown. A map of the Huguenot strongholds shows their concentration in Aquitaine and the southern parts of the Central Plateau—precisely the areas that had become heretical in the early 13th century.

The accession of Henry of Navarre, who brought a spirit of freedom and toleration with him from the Pyrenees, was followed by the Edict of Nantes in 1598, and the 16th century ended in religious peace. But in the following century (1685) this fine edict of toleration was revoked by Louis XIV, and the Huguenots were driven from the country. France lost a valuable and progressive element of her population—to the great gain of Germany, America and Britain. She became poorer, more Catholic and more isolated than she had been, and she failed to take the leading part she might have taken in the maritime expansion of Europe. On the other hand she gained internal unity, political as well as religious. The process of centralization had gone steadily on, especially under Richelieu, and it has remained the dominant feature of French political life ever since.

2 *The French Frontiers*

The Pyrenees now became, with the addition of Roussillon to France in 1659, the frontier with Spain along their whole length. In the south-east the Alps already formed the boundary, though the Nice country and that part of Savoy west of the watershed did not come in until 1860. But the main expansion of France at this time was towards the Rhine. She had long possessed almost all the country west of the Meuse draining to the Seine, but beyond, in the hills and vales of Lorraine, the Holy Roman Empire still held sway, in dangerous proximity to the Paris basin. The aim of France was to reach the Rhine, which was conceived as the ideal limit in this direction and remembered as the frontier of Imperial Rome.

France was unified and organized: the hill country was divided and disorganized; and the first step in the expansion was the acquisition of the territories of the Three Bishoprics (Metz, Toul, Verdun). By the end of the century Alsace, which could be approached independently by way of the Gate of Burgundy, and much of Lorraine, became incorporated in France. This north-eastern frontier, despite some swinging to and fro since that time, is today much the same as it was in the 17th century.

The 18th century was on the whole a time of peace. The growth of overseas commerce and maritime enterprise did not affect France as much as it affected Britain. The agrarian changes which revolutionized agriculture in Britain had no such dramatic effects on French life. In Britain, with her risky harvests, the introduction of root-crops from Holland encouraged enclosure and favoured stock raising, but French agriculture was more stable, thanks to her good farming and her firmly-established peasantry. Moreover, the continuity of social life was not imperilled by the attractions of manufacturing industry, which was encouraged and developed in Britain by overseas trade and by her wealth in coal and iron.

3 *Revolution*

Political revolution came to France, it is true, but it strengthened the underlying continuity of the peasant tradition by getting rid of the Frankish nobility. The weakness of the country gentry offers a strong contrast to the virility of the peasant tradition and of its social expressions, the village and market-town. The Industrial Revolution had nothing like the overwhelming importance it had in Britain. The French coal-fields are small and scattered, and though there have been important recent developments in other sources of power, industry has tended to retain the character and personality of former days. With this, there has been continuity of skill and craftsmanship in occupations and trades often based on the hereditary principle. Local industries that were wiped out in Britain by large-scale production survive in France—in small metallurgical centres, woollen or tanning towns, pottery centres and so on. Such a scheme, which relegates production for export to a secondary position, may seem strange and old-fashioned to our eyes, but to the French it is both natural and proper, and it is important to realize that the two points of view have grown out of differences in the two environments. Times of international stress, when trade is necessarily restricted, have tended to throw into relief some of the strong points of the French system.

The utilization of electricity derived from water power has brought new opportunities to parts of France: indeed much pioneer work in the application of hydro-electric power to industry was carried out in the French Alps. The Pyrenees are also important in this direction, and the electrification of railways was first completed in the south-west. The full development of "white coal", however, belongs to the period since the Second World War. For developments in the Rhône valley, see p. 168.

4 Communications

RAILWAYS The railways and other means of communication illustrate very clearly the centralized control of Paris. Almost all the railway systems have their main termini here. The Société Nationale des Chemins de Fer Français has controlled all rail communications since 1938. There are five regions. The Chemin de Fer du Nord feeds the industrial area about Lille and the adjoining Channel ports; the Réseau de l'Est serves Lorraine and the eastern part of the Paris basin; the Sud-Est system (formerly the P.L.M.) provides a direct link with the Midi; the Chemin de Fer de l'Ouest covers the north-west; and the Sud-Ouest runs to Nantes, Bordeaux and Limoges. It is interesting to observe that, despite the natural and strategic concentration of railways on Paris, the need for direct communication between the Straits of Dover and the Alps has renewed the former importance of Reims.

WATER TRANSPORT The Paris basin and the industrial areas of the north-east are the regions of France that make most use of water transport. The river system centring on Paris provides excellent means of transport linked up with the tidal estuary of the Seine at Rouen and with the northern coal-field by way of the Oise and Marne and connecting canals. The Seine system is also connected with those of the Rhine, Saône-Rhône and Loire, but the shifting bed of the Loire and the velocity and irregular flow of the Rhône have made those rivers relatively unimportant for transport. For the Rhône, see p. 168.

The new Rove canal tunnel, running west from Marseille to the Étang de Berre, has opened up a great harbour and industrial centre in and around that lake, developing as an extension of Marseille. Parts of a Rhône lateral canal which will take large vessels up to Lyon have been constructed. The Canal du Midi from Toulouse to Cette is shallow, and though it makes possible through-communication from the Mediterranean to the Atlantic it is used for local traffic only.

The maintenance of canal-transport in general is related to the natural ease of construction over low watersheds and to the fact that the location of industries and harvests (e.g., wines) necessitates the conveyance of bulky cargoes. An outstanding point is the way in which canals have intensified the natural concentration of communications in the Paris basin. Dimensional uniformity of all main canals is secured by an Act passed in 1879.

ROADS The magnificent road system of modern France has grown out of the *Voies Postales* organized by Colbert in the 17th century and developed under Louis XV in the 18th. The strategic motive, exaggerating the affinities of nature, is evident in the remarkable position occupied by Paris in relation to these roads. Historical and political forces have constantly added their weight to the centralizing power of the capital. Air France, the nationalized air transport system, inevitably has its headquarters there.

5 *Population*

The dominant position of Paris is quite unchallenged. The capital city, with 2,790,000 people (or 7,400,000, including the suburban areas), is the only centre in the north with more than 250,000 inhabitants. Nantes and Strasbourg, the only other northern towns to approach that figure, are distant between 200 and 250 miles from Paris. Only Marseille (778,000) and

Lyon (529,000) pass the half-million mark, and only six French cities (including Nice, Toulouse and Bordeaux) exceed 250,000. This contrasts very strongly with Germany. France has only 30 centres over 100,000: West Germany, with less than half the area, has 56 (see p. 182 for urban populations).

The proportion between rural and urban populations emphasizes the differences between France and her highly industrialized neighbours. In England and Wales 80 per cent of the total population is urban, and the average density exceeds 800 per square mile. In France the section of population classed as rural, though declining, is 40 per cent, and the population density is less than 220 per square mile. The tendency towards urbanization, however, is increasing, and many social problems are related to this change. The dominance of Paris is becoming still more pronounced; the population of the Seine department increased by nearly 50 per cent in ten years. Marseille and Lyon have increased quite slowly. A remarkable feature of French demography is the uniformity of size among groups of regional capitals (see p. 182).

Rural depopulation has reached serious dimensions in western, southern and central France, generally in the poor upland districts. In the first quarter of this century, the department of Lozère lost 23 per cent of its inhabitants, Basses Alpes 22 per cent, Nièvre 18 per cent, Ardèche, Ariège and Gers 17 per cent, Mayenne, Tarn et Garonne 16 per cent, while in the Central Plateau as a whole most of the departments lost over 10 per cent of their population. Moreover, many of the departments that show an increase owe it mainly to the immigration of aliens. In 1926 there were over 3,000,000 foreigners in France (mainly Italians and Poles) but the number had fallen to less than 2,000,000 in 1962. Spaniards, Portuguese and Algerians are now the leading immigrants. The death-rate in France is fairly high, and the infant mortality remarkably high when compared with that of Britain. One of the factors here is the difficulty of sanitation and welfare work among a population so largely rural. The population of France would actually have fallen between the World Wars if it had not been for immigration. Since Social Security was introduced in 1945, with generous family allowances, the trend has been reversed. The current population increase of 1·5 per cent is the highest on record. (The 1965 population was estimated at nearly 50 millions.)

6 *Trade*

By tradition France is protectionist, but she has none-the-less taken the lead in setting up the European Economic Community (Common Market). Foreign trade statistics have been liable to fluctuations and are difficult to interpret, but her leading imports have tended to be coal, wine, wool, oil, cereals, cotton and machinery; her exports chemical products, iron and steel, textiles, automobiles and wine. Three-quarters of her total exports are manufactured goods. The United Kingdom used to be her largest customer—mainly for wines and brandy —but that position is now held by Germany. Altogether 47 per cent of French exports go to Common Market countries and 45 per cent of imports come from them. As late as 1955 the value of trade with the colonies was one-third of both imports and exports: trade with the Franc Zone has not declined in amount but is now about one-quarter of the total, greatly exceeded by that within the Common Market.

7 *Government and Administration*

After a period of great prosperity from 1926 to 1931, the economic depression brought difficulties for France as for the rest of Europe. The revival of strong nationalist feeling in Germany and many other countries strengthened France's demand for adequate safeguards against invasion. But weakened by internal dissensions she could not resist the military might of Hitler's Germany in 1940. Her position, geographically and historically, gives her opportunities of co-operation, and the task of giving Europe a lead towards a new order has fallen to her lot. The idealism of Jean Monnet found its first expression in the Schuman Plan (1950) proposing a common authority for Western Europe's coal and steel industries (see p. 183). France's economic recovery has been such that she now ranks fifth among the world's nations in industrial output.

Internally France has had to face political as well as social and economic difficulties, and her parliamentary system, borrowed in the first place from Britain, has had to be considerably revised.[1] The persistent demand for administrative decentralization, which is over a century old, has been partly met, e.g., by the creation of a score of military districts. There is no doubt that the 90 Napoleonic departments are too small for many purposes, and as a rule they correspond to no natural groupings of population.

The "regional" movement would base administration on 21 regions.[2] Yet centralization seems to suit France: it has strong geographic and historic forces behind it and the supremacy of Paris is unchallenged. There are some 38,000 Communes which need supervision and financial assistance from above; 63 per cent of them have less than 500 inhabitants. These villages and small towns form a network of varied and thriving communities, closely knit with the rural background of the provinces. Though now threatened by many forces, this long intimacy has left its stamp on the whole structure of French civilization.

[1] A new Constitution was introduced by the Fourth Republic of France in 1946, but it did not bring about political stability: there were no less than *twelve* cabinets between Dec. 1946 and Dec. 1952. It is interesting to note for comparison with Great Britain that over seven million smallholders and farm-workers—a third of the working population—were the largest single pressure group in the political life of France. Lack of popular support for the government's Algerian policy was a major difficulty. In 1958 unrest in Algeria provoked a serious political crisis in France, and the war-time leader of Free France, General de Gaulle, was called in to assume power and attempt a solution of the Algerian problem. Under the constitution of the Fifth Republic (1958), establishing the French Community, the African colonies were given territorial self-government with the right to opt for independence (see Chapter 22). The new régime was pledged "to bring about economic and financial recovery and to reaffirm France's position among the great countries of the world". The presidential powers were widened, the use of the referendum was authorized, and an essential measure of political stability assured.

[2] The regions, each with a prefect in charge, are essentially the old Provinces of France or subdivisions of them. Much planning is being undertaken on the basis of regions (but see note on p. 168) and the 5th four-year plan comes into operation in 1966. For purposes of local education administration France is divided into 17 academic areas. It is of interest to note that a law on the teaching and the use of dialects and regional languages was passed in 1951. It allows them to be used in school instruction. The law is at present confined to Basque, Breton, Catalan and Provençal.

Chapter 11

LANGUAGE, LITERATURE AND THE LAND

1 *Language and National Character*

The languages of Europe have played an important part in the evolution of modern nations. Indeed language has come to be the index of nationality in most countries, although Switzerland may remind us that there can be national harmony without linguistic unity. Languages are perhaps the most direct expression of national character, and much has been written of the revelation of Britain's personality in her free flexible English tongue.

It is probably true to say that nowhere else in the world have language and literature played anything like the same rôle as among the French. French language and literature conform to rules which throw much light on French character. Logic and clarity are their outstanding virtues; the evolution of the language has been governed by intellectual laws. French pronunciation, too, is clear and precise; the vowels are simple and happily balanced with the consonants; the syllables carry equal value; moderation and measure are always in evidence. And as the language reveals the nature of the French character so the literature of France has evolved in harmony with the traditions of the nation. The centralized pattern of France runs through her life and literature.

We saw in Chapter 9 how the dialects of French fall into two groups, those of the southern half of the country (known collectively as the Langue d'Oc) being nearer to their Latin parent than those of the north (Langue d'Oil). Among the latter dialects it was the language spoken in the Paris region (called *Francien*) that came to predominate as the literary form; and since the 15th century the other dialects have ceased to be means of literary expression. The supremacy of Francien must be related to the gathering of intellectual movements about the Capetian court and to the prestige of the great University of Paris. It ultimately rests, therefore, on the geographical and historical forces which occasioned the rise of Paris as the political and artistic capital of the region. Once established in literature, the Francien tongue spread slowly as the standard language of the country, evolving in accordance with certain logical rules.

2 Epic Literature

When we turn to the origins of literature we are in a mysterious world where legend and folk-lore mingle with historic record. But although much of this legendary background of European life is probably due to the play of fancy, it is now realized that there may be a substantial basis of fact in the old tales. Many stories which relate to a glorious Golden Age and to a subsequent time of misery may perpetuate folk-memory of climatic change in prehistoric Europe. The Bronze Age (the age of "golden" metal) is believed to have been a period of warmth and plenty, whereas the Early Iron Age which followed was a time of damp cold and poverty for Europe north of the Alps. The wanderings of peoples, notably of Celtic-speaking peoples, occasioned by this time of climatic stress would evoke heroic legends of the type frequently embodied in folk-lore.

The oldest literary form of the French language is to be found in the mediaeval epics. The epics of Arthurian romance are steeped in Celtic tradition and incorporate much dim legend with some historical truths. The Chansons de Geste form another important group dealing with historic events and traditional episodes, many of them associated with the struggles of Christian heroes against Saracen invaders. The most famous epic poem, the Chanson de Roland, which has been described as "a masterpiece of poetry and the first great monument of French literature", turns upon the defeat of Roland, Charlemagne's nephew, on the field of Roncesvalles in the year 778. The location of this Pyrenean tragedy on one of the vital defensive frontiers of Christendom helps to explain the deep significance of the theme. During the 11th and 12th centuries the Chansons won wide popularity, and they may be said to reflect the vigour of the rapidly expanding political and intellectual life of France.

Mediaeval France also excelled in lyrical poetry, characteristically at its best in the Midi. Here the Provençaux owed much to the influence of Arabic poetry through the medium of the Moorish invasion of Spain. Dramatic art in mediaeval times took the form of miracle plays, which were part of the Christian tradition of Europe.

3 *The Classical Period*

The Renaissance showed its influence promptly in France, thanks to the country's long and close association with the currents of Mediterranean life and thought, and the 16th century witnessed a great outburst of literary production. Within the wider unity of mediaeval Christendom a national spirit was emerging, and both language and literature were adjusted to the new outlook. Classicism—the name applied to this phase of inspiration from the Graeco-Roman world—illustrates clearly the tendency of the country to evolve according to plan, to bring intellectual order into the field of art. The prose of Rabelais mirrors faithfully the life of 16th-century France, and it has been said of him that he "laughed the Middle Ages into their grave".

A new consciousness—the sense of national unity—took the place of the mediaeval view of the universe. It had been fostered by the patriotic spirit evoked by the influence of Saint Joan (Jeanne d'Arc). Moreover, the rise of printing led to the spread of reading to a larger public, and under the influence of the Classical tradition the new literary movement, led by the King's Court, came to exert wide power in shaping the course of national development.

By the 17th century the whole life of the kingdom, political, artistic and intellectual, was focused at the court of Louis XIV. Intense patriotism and devotion to the soil of France expressed themselves in a centralized scheme of government facilitated, as we saw in previous chapters, by nature's moulding of the French landscape. Strongly classical in flavour, literature lacked the freedom of contemporary English writing. It is significant that Corneille, after bringing out *Le Cid*—with its mediaeval theme—was forced to adopt classical modes, while Boileau ignored Roland and his deeds. Similarly, linguistic standardization in France contrasts with the greater freedom of the English language, which was spread by the translation and wide circulation of the scriptures.

The French Academy, founded in the 17th century, came to be the codifier of laws governing the life and evolution of the language. We may think of an intellectual state developing as part of the centralized scheme of government. Thus unity was gained at the expense of variety and freedom, but the language was established as a logical instrument of thought, rigidly grammatical, lucid and precise. French later became the official language of diplomacy, and has remained a symbol of universal culture.

The standard language had now become the index of nationality, and French territory, after centuries of expansion, was now more or less coincident with the distribution of the language. The most serious divergences have been in that borderland which was once part of Lotharingia. Here Germanic dialects were carried west of the Rhine during the Dark Ages, and the mingling of languages has added greatly to the difficulty of finding a satisfactory frontier through this confused border belt. In Alsace the aristocracy and the townsfolk came to feel the attraction of French culture while the peasantry tended to remain German in speech if not in sentiment. The other corners of France have retained their old languages to varying degrees.[1] Catalan is spoken in Roussillon, which was part of Catalonia until 1659. Beyond the barrier of the marshy Adour, among the wooded hills of the western Pyrenees, the ancient Basque tongue keeps its hold. In the remoter parts of Brittany a Celtic language (Breton) has survived, and in the extreme north of the country, around Dunkirk, a Low German dialect, Flemish, is found. Moreover, in France south of about the 46th parallel some regions still retain their Langue d'Oc dialects, notably Provence. Corsica has its own dialect of Italian. Despite these interesting survivals, standard French

[1] See Fig. 3, p. 17.

has long been current almost everywhere. Its general adoption has been helped by social causes such as the French Revolution, improved communications in the 19th century, and military conscription.

4 *The Romantic Movement; Modern France*

The 18th century produced the genius of Rousseau, whose writings had great influence on the French Revolution and on the growth of democratic thought. His delight in nature and his interest in high mountains must surely owe something to his birthplace in Geneva, between the Jura and the High Alps.

The full tide of Romanticism came to France after the disturbances of the Revolutionary and the Napoleonic periods. It was coincident with a marked growth of travel and foreign influence. It brought a new interest in nature and in the life of man set against the background of nature, and it turned for inspiration to the Middle Ages and their chivalric splendour. The names of Roland and Roncesvalles, almost forgotten for four centuries, reappear in literature, and with them comes a new interest in regional life; *Le Cor* of Alfred de Vigny echoes the hunting horn of the Pyrenean heights as well as the epic horn of Roland. Much of the work of Victor Hugo shows his interest in local life and landscape and helped to develop the sense of history and locality in much the same way as did the writings of Walter Scott in Britain. Later on, the literature of other countries was ransacked and many new fields were exploited as communications improved and interests broadened. Leconte de Lisle, for example, turned to Celtic and Finnish sources and to his native tropics for poetic subjects.

In the novel of the mid-19th century the works of George Sand and Balzac stand out on account of their regional interest. Balzac's descriptions of the thrifty peasants of the Loire and George Sand's charming studies of Berry and La Vallée Noire helped to interest people in local characteristics. Pierre Loti, attracted by the life of the sea, has left us notable descriptions of the Breton fishermen (*Pêcheurs d'Islande*) and their intangible world, and also of the Basque peasants. Alphonse Daudet, in the south, dealt with the extravangances of his fellow-men of the Midi in *Tartarin de Tarascon* and its companion volumes, where the lighter side of life in sunny Provence is humorously portrayed. More recently the poet Mistral has revived the Provençal dialect, and in his pages may be found colourful pictures of the old routine of cultivation in this land of the vine and olive.

North Africa, as part of the Mediterranean world, has long stimulated literary interest, and since the war of 1914–18 there has been a considerable growth of what may be called French-African literature. This has taken many forms: both lyrical and descriptive works, and also studies of negro psychology and folk-lore. Nor should we omit mention of the school of literary production that has developed independently in French Canada.

Modern French literature is vigorous and its high standards are faithfully upheld. Perhaps the outstanding character is the high general level maintained. French literature has been compared to a well-ordered garden, and the student will have in mind the garden-like landscape of the country itself. The old heritage of law and order and universality seems to dominate language, literature and the land.

In painting as in the art of dress designing Paris still ranks as the world's first city. France has repeatedly given a lead in art and in architecture. Georges Duhamel once described her as a laboratory in which the raw materials of morals, art and philosophy are prepared for universal use. Writers of the stature of Proust and Gide have world-wide currency, and the French cinema as well as the stage, both commercial and state-aided, have exerted international influence. In French public esteem the highest place is held by the artist, writer, philosopher and man of the theatre; several fields of activity may be covered by a Cocteau or a Sartre. Paris houses the headquarters of U.N.E.S.C.O., a location which symbolizes the prestige of intellectual life and of the creative arts in France.

PART III

THE REGIONS OF FRANCE

Chapter 12

INTRODUCTION

It has frequently been remarked that France shows a rare combination of strong national unity and regional variety. In the previous chapters we have traced the evolution of nature and of human society working in nature's setting, and we have tried to show how, together, through the centuries, they have moulded the character and personality of the country. The chapters that follow will describe the main regions of modern France in more detail than has been possible in the general surveys. In the belief that it is artificial to attempt to understand the life of man apart from his environment, we shall keep our attention directed continuously to both aspects of geographical study.

It must not be imagined that the regions we have chosen represent the only way of subdividing the country geographically. There is endless variety in nature, and each of our regions, as we shall have occasion to point out, falls into numerous subregions which may have considerable individuality and independence of local life. It should be remembered, too, that the boundaries between regions are never fixed lines but always zones of transition. Having selected the units of study, we should endeavour to obtain a picture of life in those regions, bearing in mind that the picture is of more value and interest than the frame around it.

The climatic variations naturally have special importance in determining the regional variety of a country still essentially agricultural. We have already sketched the general distribution of vegetation, natural and cultivated: we described them together in the same chapter, because in a country so "profoundly humanized" as France it is often impossible to separate the results of the hand of man from the work of nature. Her soils have been the source of her strength for centuries, and ages of forest clearing have transformed the original landscape. We are liable to forget how gradually the riches of

Figure 15 The Regions of France

her fields and gardens have accumulated. An English traveller, Arthur Young, noted in 1789 that neither clover, chicory, turnips, sprouts, beetroot nor potatoes paid tithes, "because they were new produce". Though there have been continual introductions of new crops to the fields of France—we may mention here buckwheat (*sarrasin*), which takes its name from the Saracens—the fundamental controls of nature have not changed. Increasing specialization with improvements of transport methods has rather intensified the operation of natural laws.

On the whole, too, there is close agreement between the human regions of the country and the physical divisions. Only in the east and north-east (Burgundy and Alsace-Lorraine) is it difficult to define with precision regions which have nevertheless distinct human and historic individuality. We have already noted many of the human differences between north France and south. Physically, while the north is a vast lowland area with fringing uplands, the south consists of a Central Plateau flanked by two separated river basins from which the land rises again to the Alps and Pyrenees (Fig. 15).

The south is more diversified than the north: its alternating highlands and lowlands give five physical regions characterized by fairly sharp limits and corresponding individuality of climate, vegetation and outlook. The north has neither the sharp barriers of high fold-mountains and scarped plateau, nor the variety of coasts that turn west, south and south-east to the Atlantic and Mediterranean. The north has a variety of its own, but (in the words of Vidal de la Blache) it is made up of subtle shades rather than of sharp contrasts.

Yet the lowlands of Languedoc and the Gate of Carcassonne have permitted easy communications around the southern end of the Central Plateau. Between north and south, similarly, the regions grade one into the other. The south-west has lowland connections with the Paris basin and also with Brittany. The upper basins of Allier and Loire have carried northern influences into the plateau, while east and west movements along its northern edge are a very old feature. The most critical region of contact between north and south lies where the upper Saône meets the scarps of the Côte d'Or and the Plateau de Langres. This region is Burgundy, the link between the north and the Midi.

The subsequent chapters are based on the following nine regions which are shown in Fig. 15.

1. The Paris Basin.
2. Armorica (Brittany and its borders).

3. Alsace-Lorraine.
4. Burgundy.
5. The Central Plateau.
6. The Basin of Aquitaine.
7. The Pyrenees.
8. The Mediterranean Coast and the Lower Rhône.
9. The French Alps.

To these we shall add a chapter on Corsica and the former French colonies.

Chapter 13

THE PARIS BASIN

1 *The River System*

We have seen in earlier chapters how the concentration of
river courses towards the centre of the Paris basin has helped
to give the region unity. Thanks to erosion by the Seine and
its tributaries—Yonne, Aube, Marne, Oise and Aisne—the
series of concentric outcrops of sedimentary rocks is most complete in the eastern half of the basin; and we can trace successively the Pleistocene *limon* of the Beauce, the various Tertiary deposits ending in the Falaise de l'Ile de France, the
broad Cretaceous outcrop of dry Champagne, the low and
still well-wooded impermeable clays of the Champagne
Humide.

Northwards this wet strip passes into the more elevated
Argonne, a difficult forested area of great strategic importance
in France's many wars with Germany. All this belt, in fact, has
acted as a barrier and helped, in conjunction with the out-
ward-facing limestone scarps, to check intrusion into the basin
from the east. Beyond comes the higher land of the Jurassic
rocks, cut longitudinally by the Meuse towards the north but
opening out in the south-east as the Plateau of Langres, dissected transversely by the Seine and the Aube. Between the
Argonne and the Meuse it forms the wooded Côtes de Meuse,
on the borders of Lorraine.

The Seine river-system thus defines pretty clearly the limits
of the basin on the east. The middle Loire region, on the south
and south-west, is physically and humanly part of the basin of
Paris. But beyond Berry, Poitou and Anjou we pass into the
Central Plateau, Aquitaine and Armorica. To the west, Palaeozoic rocks outcrop along a line that runs from about Bayeux
to Angers, and here the Armorican region begins.

In the western section of the basin, the ancient folded core of north Brittany, though buried, gives rise to a doming of the sedimentary deposits which cover it. This forms the upland known as the Collines de Normandie and the Collines du Perche. The water-parting that they occasion breaks the symmetry of the drainage of the basin, which here goes independently to the English Channel on the north and into the Loire on the south.

Beyond the lower Seine, too, a number of short rivers, as well as the longer Somme, drain direct to the Channel along deep trenches related to rock folds formed parallel to the Artois ridge. This series of chalk scarps and valleys, acting as a check to movement from north-east to south-west, acquired tragic fame in the war of 1914–18. The chalk girdle meets the Channel abruptly along nearly the whole length of this coast, but in the Boulonnais (the projecting nose which ends in Cap Gris Nez) the eroded summit of the earth-fold that runs from the Weald to the Artois brings older rocks to the surface. The Artois ridge drops to the south-east before we meet the older rocks rising again in the Ardennes, and over this low sill (*Seuil de Vermandois*) the basins of Brussels and of Paris are connected by some of the busiest lines of communication in Europe.

The annual rainfall map brings out very clearly the concentric plan of the basin. The Channel coast, the Normandy Heights and the high rim on the south and east receive over 35 inches of rain in many places. As one goes towards Paris the rainfall decreases and the interior has less than 25 inches over an area roughly corresponding to that of the Tertiary exposures. The maximum precipitation comes in early summer and autumn; spring is dry (Fig. 6).

2 Paris

Within this structural, topographical and climatic unity there is a surprising variety of local landscape and life. We may take as a starting-point the great city which is in some ways the world's finest capital. Paris lies immediately below the junction of Seine and Marne, between the curving river and the denuded scarps and isolated "monts" (e.g. Montmartre) of the Tertiary plateau. The Seine divides into two arms over the alluvial floor of the valley, and a small island thus formed—the Ile de la Cité—was the nucleus of the earliest known settlement made in this corn-growing area; it became the Roman *Lutetia*. The island provided defence, but it also facilitated the crossing of the river, and the Roman road to the north made use of it. Other settlements in the north of France, however, were at that time far more important than Paris.

It was when valley routes and river traffic were reviving after the Dark Ages, and agricultural, commercial and political life was expanding, that Paris became the meeting-place and capital of the neighbourhood. Today it dominates not only its region and the north in general, but the whole of France in a unique way. It is the centre of nearly every aspect of French life—political, administrative, industrial, financial, commercial, educational, artistic. The replacement of its old circular fortifications by boulevards gives the city a distinctive plan, but the busiest roads are still those which carry traffic from east to west and from north to south along lines that are centuries old.

Most of the famous historic buildings of Paris are near the centre along the Seine; the commercial districts are largely around the intersection of the two main axes; the industrial parts lie in the outer fringes and suburbs. The industries are extremely varied but in many ways typical of an old metropolitan centre. Chief among its products are: prepared foodstuffs, chemicals, glass, fine porcelain (Sèvres), leather goods and jewellery. The motor-car industry is highly important and the book and printing trades are characteristic of a great centre of education and culture.

Nor should it be forgotten that Paris is a port of considerable size; there are 8 miles of navigable river within the city. Coal and building materials form the bulk of the cargoes imported.

The immediate neighbourhood of the city is largely given up to market-gardening. The French term for this (*cultures maracîhères*) is derived from the fact that cultivation of this type was formerly carried on in a district—le Marais, now the Jewish quarter—which was once marshy.

3 *The "Pays"*

Farther afield we come to the Tertiary plateaux lying between the convergent streams and forming sub-regions or *pays* of distinct individuality. Such, to give them their popular names, are Beauce, Brie, Sologne and Valois. Beauce lies south-west of Paris and stretches almost to the Loire. The permeable limestone table-land is in this area covered by a thin layer of *limon*. It is one of the most famous wheat-lands of Europe: "valuable as a farm in Beauce" is a proverb in France. Settlement depends on deep costly wells and the population is concentrated in villages or large fortress-like farms. There are no big towns. Chartres, its historic capital, is on the river Eure at its north-western edge. Dairying has become very important.

Brie lies across the Seine to the north-east of Beauce. The limestone is thinner here and the country well supplied with water. Scattered farms are abundant and agriculture more varied if not so rich. Provins is the old capital, but Melun on the Seine is more important today.

Sologne, lying within the bend of the Loire, is very different. Its lake-studded clay soils have only slowly and partially yielded to cultivation and afforestation. The great route-town and market-centre of Orléans (Roman *Cenabum Aureliani*) occupies a strategic site at the elbow of the Loire, where the river comes within easy reach of Paris across the open level Beauce.

Valois is situated north of the lower Marne. It has a good deal of richly-cultivated loam and is diversified by heights clothed with woods of oak, beech and hornbeam. Soissonnais and Tardenois are adjoining *pays* of this north-eastern extension of the Tertiaries.

Rising from beneath these central deposits, the chalk girdle is widest on the east and north, but very narrow on the south. Its chief divisions are—Caux, Picardy, Artois and Champagne. We begin with Caux and the Lower Seine.

The ancient bridge-town of Rouen lies on a curve of the Seine where it cuts a picturesque course of entrenched meanders through an extensive chalk plateau to reach the sea. Rouen still has the air of a quiet market-town and regional capital, but it has become a great industrial centre and the *entrepôt* for the overseas trade of much of northern France. Its textile industries grew out of the household weaving of a natural sheep-rearing district. Industry later migrated to the valleys to utilize water-power and extended to imported cotton. Spinning is the main branch carried on, but weaving and dyeing are also important. Rouen imports large quantities of coal— once mainly from Britain—much of which passes upstream to Paris.

Le Havre, the deep-water port at the entrance to the Seine estuary, is of modern growth and of much more than local importance. It not only imports coal and cotton and wool but acts as an *entrepôt* for tropical products such as coffee and sugar. Both Le Havre and Rouen have oil refineries.

The plateau south and west of the lower Seine has *limon* covering it and is crossed by deep valleys occupied by rivers flowing north, of which the Eure is the largest. This country falls into a number of *pays* which preserve the character and the architectural wealth of mediaeval cornlands.

To the north of Rouen and the Seine estuary is Caux, highlying, fertile thanks to its surface loams, and cultivated almost everywhere. Its shut-in orchards and tree-protected homesteads seek shelter from the salty gales of the Channel, above which its cliff edges tower. The early settlements of the Norsemen along the Seine valley became focal points for Caux, the swift streams flowing down on this side providing power for textile mills. Caudebec is the best known of these small towns: *bec* is but one of many Norse place-names.

The river Béthune, with Dieppe at its mouth, divides the Pays de Caux from Picardy, another massive slab of chalk traversed by numerous dry valleys and by the marshy flats of the Somme, whose willows and poplars make a forest by contrast with the dry table-lands above. Coverings of loam are abundant, however, and they yield heavy crops of wheat and sugar-beet. Much of this region was devastated in the war of 1914–18, but it recovered with astonishing rapidity. The textile industry of St. Quentin, which used first wool, then linen and finally cotton, was soon restored to its old prosperity. The regional centre, Amiens, has its famous cathedral, its market-gardens (*hortillons*) among the little canals of the valley floor, and its old woollen industry. All this region shows a combination of rich agriculture and local industries that is typically French.

On the north-east side of Picardy is the Artois ridge, ending seawards in the distinctive little *pays* of Boulonnais. From the hills of Artois the chalk drops towards the Belgian frontier and passes under the clays and sands of the Brussels basin. Most of the drainage goes into the Scheldt system. Dunes line the flat coast, where Calais and Dunkirk ("the church among the dunes") both serve their agricultural hinterlands. Calais has developed more particularly as a packet station and Dunkirk (Dunkerque) as the port of the industrial north. It provides France with an outlet in the North Sea, is an important oil importer, and has an expanding steel industry.

The coal-field of the departments of Nord and Pas de Calais is but the western extremity of the Belgian field. It runs in a narrow belt through Valenciennes, Douai and Lens, and gives rise to a varied group of local industries. In addition much coal is exported, especially to Paris. Extensive metallurgical industries, dependent on ore imported from Lorraine, Spain and Sweden, are found both on and off the coal-field. The production of textile machinery is naturally important. The textile towns fall broadly into two groups alongside the mining centres. Lille, Tourcoing and Roubaix, formerly using local supplies of wool and flax, remain large-scale producers of woollen goods and have taken up cotton, silk and jute. The Cambrai area to the south of the coal-field specializes in fine linens (cambrics).

There have long been close relations between the chalk country of the Artois and the lowlands of French Flanders: the region, though industrialized, keeps up its rich agriculture on both plateau and plain. It has easy access to the sea and shares the density of communications (road, rail and water) and of population common to the Low Countries in general. With easy access both to the east and to the Paris basin it has for centuries been both a gateway and a zone of frontiers and bitter struggles. Its ultimate inclusion in the French kingdom has meant the addition of a part of the industrial zone of central Europe to agricultural France.

The chalklands on the east of the Paris basin are known as Champagne Pouilleuse,[1] and consist of the low plateau which is crossed by the Marne above Épernay and by the Seine below Troyes. It forms a continuation of the table-lands of Picardy and Artois, but is drier and different because of the absence of loam. The white chalk is everywhere near the surface and the vast open landscape is broken only by plantations of pines and by an occasional military camp, which emphasizes its resemblance to Salisbury Plain. Artificial fertilizers allow a certain amount of cultivation, but the life of Champagne is concentrated in the valleys that cross it; and the towns are placed either under the Tertiary scarp (Reims, Épernay) or at the foot of the chalk plateau (Troyes, Vitry-le-François). Châlons-sur-Marne, however, is centrally placed.

Streaming clays and fertile alluvial deposits made Wet Champagne a natural complement to the adjoining downland; and together they formed historic Champagne, famous for its mediaeval fairs. These fairs were held in rotation at Troyes, Provins, Arcis-sur-Aube and other centres: Troyes is said to leave its name in "Troy weight". They owed their fame partly to their local cloth trade, partly to the natural nodality and accessibility of Champagne and partly to the fact that the Counts of Champagne in the earlier Middle Ages were virtually independent of the King of France and free from restraints.

The woollen trade is still carried on at Reims and Troyes, but today the area is best known to the world for its wines. The "Champagne" wines came to the fore in the 18th century: they are produced mainly at Reims and Épernay from vineyards which line the lower slopes of the Tertiary scarp or *falaise*. Slow fermentation of the wine is obtained by storage in miles of cellars excavated in the soft rock. Both Troyes and Reims keep up their ancient function of route-towns, and

---

[1] This may be translated "beggarly". It expresses the contempt of the neighbouring countrymen for the dry parts of Champagne.

Reims, the great Roman centre, retains its prestige as an ecclesiastical capital with an archbishop.

A characteristic local metallurgical industry of Wet Champagne grew out of supplies of iron-ore extracted from the sands and of abundant fuel from the forests. St. Dizier still manufactures wire and nails.

The chalk west of the upper Seine is capped by outliers of the Tertiary sands and clays, often forested as in the Forêt d'Othe. The Pays d'Othe has the old town of Sens on the Yonne nearby. Vézelay (Pl. I) lies to the south. Mention should also be made of another ancient centre, Laon, placed on the *falaise* at the northern end of Champagne.

Turning now to the edges of the basin towards the south-west, we have, in the first place, the Jurassic belt of Champagne Berrichonne sloping up to meet the granites and schists of the Central Plateau. The drainage goes north-west by the Cher, Indre, Creuse and Vienne, tributaries of the Loire; and the economic life of the area turns in the same direction towards the Touraine. The woods and pools of the Sologne shut off this Champagne Berrichonne from Orléans. Berry formed in the past a great passage-way between Burgundy and Aquitaine, but as new currents of circulation developed its use declined. It has remained largely agricultural. Wheat and sheep are its typical products, and it has the vine in places. Urban life is not rich, but Bourges has been a route-centre since Roman days. Its great cathedral stands on a bluff almost surrounded by water. Poitiers, on a tributary of the Vienne, is the historic gate-town of Poitou, by which the Paris basin communicates with Aquitaine. Because of its position it has been affected by many of the movements of man and culture between north and south in France.

Near Blois the Loire leaves the Tertiary deposits and widens its flood-plain. Well-mixed soils make the valley very productive and its sunny slopes are under the vine. It broadens still more below Tours, where routes from the south cross the river. Touraine is the region where the streams of Berry converge, isolating patches of Tertiary rocks which add to the variety of a charming countryside. This is "the garden of France", and

also "the land of castles". At its lower limit is Anjou, where
Saumur is noted for its sparkling wines.

Between Touraine and the Seine Bay lies the western mar-
gin of the Paris basin. Streams flowing from the Normandy

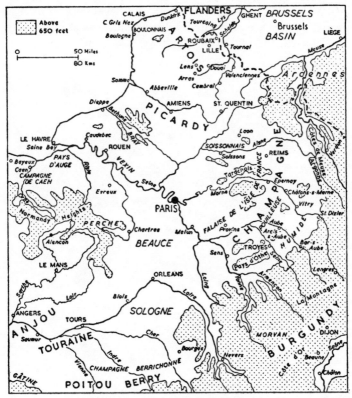

Figure 16 The Paris Basin

Heights have cut deeply into limestone and chalk so as to
form many distinctive little blocks of country or *pays*. Woods
and pastures are common on the higher and wetter parts, but
in the Campagne de Caen, towards the coast at the limit of
the basin, the Jurassic rim widens out to form a notable

stretch of fertile cornland. Caen, joined to the sea by a short canal, has many memories of Norman times, and more recently its historic links with Britain were forged anew in the Normandy landings which led to the final overthrow of Germany in 1945. It exports agricultural produce and iron-ore, and an ancient local iron industry has been revived and developed on modern lines. The ores are associated with the older rocks of the edge of Armorica, the region to which we now turn.

Chapter 14

ARMORICA (BRITTANY AND ITS BORDERS)

1 General Character

We include under the name Armorica[1] not only Brittany proper but also its fringing regions: the Cotentin, the Bocage Normand, the Bocages[2] of Maine and Anjou, the Vendée and the Nantes region. These form the continental base of the Breton peninsula, regions of transition, in many ways, between Brittany and the interior of France; but the whole has geological unity.

Whereas in the Paris basin the surface rocks are everywhere younger than the Lias period, in Armorica they are mostly Palaeozoic, often metamorphosed and interrupted by long lines of gneiss and granite which converge, as we saw in Chapter 2, towards the west. This land of ancient and for the most part infertile rocks has been, in human affairs, a region of poverty and difficulty. Its once mountainous surface has been worn down by ages of erosion, and a peneplain has resulted, revealing the inmost layers of the Hercynian folds.

The earth movements of Tertiary times caused a minor uplift which allowed renewed erosion to carve out the slight irregularities of the present surface. Since then the region has sunk somewhat, so that the drowned coasts are very indented (Pl. VI), and lined with small islands.

The drainage streams out in all directions from the impermeable surface of the peninsula, in complete contrast to the drainage of the Paris basin. Of many small streams flowing north to the Channel the Rance is the chief. It has St. Malo and Dinard on its large drowned estuary. The Blavet goes

---

[1] This name is taken from the Roman term for the region: Celtic *ar* = on and *mor* = sea.

[2] *Bocage:* the name given to a landscape of hedge-lined fields, typical of pastoral regions, often on impermeable rocks.

south to Hennebont and Lorient; its head-waters drain the middle section of the depression which has been formed in the relatively soft shales and clayey schists between the two main girders of the peninsula. The western end of this depression is occupied by the river Aulne, whose valley is continued in a long fiord-like inlet, the Rade de Brest. Carboniferous rocks have been preserved in this valley, which is sometimes referred to as the basin of Châteaulin or of Finistère.

But it is in the basin of Rennes that the central depression is best developed. The Vilaine takes the drainage out to the south, but its tributaries show very clearly the east-west grain of the land. Here and there the valleys narrow, in characteristic "Appalachian" way, as the streams cut across hard ribs of sandstone. Such lines of sandstone or granite, revealed by erosion, give Brittany what relief it now has. They reach their maximum development in the Monts d'Arrée (1,300 feet) and the Montagnes Noires, north and south respectively of the basin of Châteaulin. Corresponding to the greater height and extent of the Monts d'Arrée, the northern coastal platform is higher than the southern, and there has been more subsidence along the north. The Channel Islands are the surviving parts of former land extension here.

Shallow seas open to the Atlantic and long funnel-shaped estuaries make Brittany a region of strong currents and great tidal range. In places the sea almost disappears from view at low tide, and the tidal range may be as much as 40 feet. Not only has this given opportunity for small vessels to find their way far up the rivers, but it has given France the first tidal power station in the world, in the Rance estuary. It results also in a marginal belt of rich marine life, of seaweed, shellfish and fish. The harvest of the sea is doubly valuable because it includes sand and seaweed for manuring the land, as well as fish of many kinds.

The sea has a strong controlling influence on the climate. The winters are very mild and the summers, especially in the coastlands, temperate (average temperatures, January: 43° F.; July: 65° F.). Rain is general and fairly heavy, with a characteristic maritime maximum in autumn. Cloudiness and strong

winds are further features of the climate. The long and early
spring is important for Breton agriculture.

Armorica keeps a good deal of its forest cover, once widespread except on the exposed coasts. Man's interference has
converted most of the interior forest into *bocage*; the countryside is parcelled into a chess-board of small fields with abundant hedgerow timber and frequent breaks of bracken, broom,
gorse and low forest. Scattered homesteads take the place of
villages through this well-watered but impoverished landscape.

There is a clear distinction between the interior (Arcoet,
i.e., the country of the woods) and the coastlands (Armor). But
before describing these regions a glance at the past will help
us to understand the life of a peninsula which is full of ancient
customs.

2 The Past

Brittany received its first civilization from the south with the
expansion of prehistoric trade along the sea-ways of western
Europe. This "megalithic" culture blossomed in the early days
of metal: gold and tin were found in the sands along the south
coast, and several kinds of useful and attractive hard stones
were sought after for making tools and ornaments. Thousands
of great stone monuments remain as evidence of this prehistoric activity; they are unusually elaborate and abundant in
the department of Morbihan, notably around Carnac. Morbihan means "little sea", and takes its name from the island-
studded inlet south of Vannes, a sheltered harbour for the
small ships of old.

But by the time iron had come into use, other parts of western
Europe had taken the lead, and they were to become increasingly prosperous and attractive. With the expansion of Greek
and later of Roman civilization trade routes across eastern
France became definitely established, and the peninsular position of Brittany, so important in the early days of sea-faring,
now meant isolation and stagnation. Thus the remote west
was left to itself, to brood over its past and look out to the sea;
the Romans were not greatly interested in this damp corner
of Gaul.

In the Dark Ages refugees from south-western Britain gave Brittany both its name and its Celtic language, and Christianity came from the same overseas source. The Celtic Saints founded churches which often became the nuclei of settlements, but the peasants clung to their superstitions, and their reverence for the great stone monuments lived on in Christian guise. The pilgrim movement brought the old sea-ways into use once more during the Middle Ages, and Brittany became the half-way-house between Ireland and north-west Spain. This transit function was maintained when, in the 14th century, commerce began to expand in the northern seas and the Italian galleys came round by sea to Flanders. As Atlantic shipping developed, the daring Breton sailors took an early part in the voyages to the Newfoundland banks. It was not until 1491 that Brittany became part of the French kingdom. In many ways the peninsula has remained a region apart, facing out towards the sea rather than in towards Paris.

3 Arcoet

The interior, as we have seen, is mostly *bocage*. The damp climate and poor soils make agriculture difficult, but grass-land is abundant and cattle-rearing is the main activity of the scattered farmsteads. Considerable use is made of the oak for domestic purposes, and the charcoal-burner may still be found at work. Scanty as the population is, it has streamed out, since the middle of last century, to Paris and other large cities.

East of the Blavet and of St. Brieuc the land falls gradually to the basin of Rennes, and French becomes the universal language of the people. East Brittany is more open to the influences of the outside world. In the valley of the Vilaine wheat tends to replace buckwheat and rye. Rennes, near the centre of that basin, is Brittany's only inland town of any size: it is the regional capital, route- and market-centre, and University town.

4 Armor

The coastal parts of Brittany are much more densely peopled than the interior. Fishing and trade bring new resources, but agriculture too is richer and more varied. The soils are poor enough, except for patches of *limon* along the north coast (in Léon and Trégorrois), but shelly sands and seaweed are available to lighten the clays and to enrich the lighter soils. In the shallow bay of St. Michel much fertile land has been reclaimed. Intensive cultivation has made the north coast a great producer of early vegetables and fruit—strawberries, artichokes, peas, potatoes, onions and salads—for the markets of Paris and London. This has been made possible by the improvement of means of communication, which have enabled the growers to take advantage of the mild spring climate of maritime Brittany. The little estuarine ports—Morlaix, St. Pol de Léon, St. Brieuc and also Pont l'Abbé in the south—have taken on a new activity as exporting centres.

But the older life of the sea still goes on. St. Malo and Paimpol send boats to the Newfoundland and Icelandic grounds every year, and the south coast has deep-sea fishing for tunny in the Bay of Biscay. All around the coasts little ports are engaged in coastal fishing for herring, mackerel and flat-fish. Sailing boats are still used but the steam trawler is almost universal: much of this local fishing is carried on by men who are also small farmers.

The sardine fishery is better organized, and canning is a fairly widespread occupation. Sardines are caught in the south where the warmer waters suit them. Concarneau and Douarnenez are the chief centres concerned. Lorient, the naval port and the largest town of the south coast, derives its name from its former connection with the French East India Company. Though it has some coastal trade it is of much less importance than Brest, whose naval dockyards and commercial port lie in a sheltered harbour on the north side of the Rade de Brest. The French navy draws many of its men from Brittany.

The development of communications and of travel has enabled the peninsula to make another use of its coasts, which attract tourists in increasing numbers during the summer, by road and rail from Paris, and by airplane or boat *via* Southampton from Britain. Such economic links with the outside world are fast breaking down the isolation of Brittany, but nothing can destroy its geographical individuality.

5 *The Border Region*

The Cotentin peninsula has physical features closely resembling those of the larger peninsula. The long west coast between Mont St. Michel and Cap de la Hague is very exposed to storms. Because of its low relief it lacks the winding "rivières" and deep bays of Brittany, formed transversly to the grain of the land; and we find nothing like the same variety here. The population becomes less dense as soon as the angle of the coast changes about Avranches. Granville is the only port: it is a fishing centre and exports the early vegetables grown locally. On the north coast is Cherbourg, naval centre and port of call for American liners. Both functions are related not to any local advantage (the harbour took over a hundred years to complete) but to its situation at the end of the natural pier of Cotentin, thrown out as if to catch the shipping of the English Channel.

The east coast is sunnier, but it is short and there are no harbours worth mentioning. The interior is mainly pastoral, and cider-apple trees and buckwheat are grown.

Relief is more pronounced in the *Bocage Normand*. With that, the rainfall is heavier and grass and woodland more abundant. Many local industries survive here—bleaching, tanning, iron-working and pottery-making—and its travelling tinkers (*Bocains*) once plied their trade in many parts of France. Around its borders, where the streams provide water-power and the slopes gave defensive sites, a number of historic towns are found. Falaise, overlooking the plain of Caen, is the most famous of these. The historic province of Normandy included both the Cotentin and the bocage within its bounds, but geographically the contrast between these areas and the Seine coastlands is sharp and real.

The bocages of Maine and of Anjou occupy the basin of the southward-flowing river Mayenne. Topographically it is the eastward continuation of the basin of Rennes. Woods, heaths and pastures are still prevailing features of the landscape, but wheat becomes more important. Before the river reaches the

Loire it passes Angers on its right bank. This old border city, now a manufacturing centre, occupies a strategic site guarding the passage from the Paris basin to Brittany. Hence the historic significance of Anjou; the ancestors of the Capets were marquises of Anjou.

Figure 17 Armorica

South of the lower Loire is the Vendée, a continuation of the southern coast-plateau of Brittany, crossed by the low granite ridge of the Gâtine. Rough moorland here alternates with warm valleys that have the vine. Buckwheat is grown, but maize appears also, and this area may be considered transitional between Brittany and the south.

There remains to be mentioned the estuarine region of the river Loire, which enters Armorica not far from Angers and cuts through the hard ridges of the Gâtine to reach the sea. Nantes occupies the site where, thanks to islands in the river, the first crossing of the estuary could be made. The Roman *Portus Namnetum* grew up at this crossing. Nantes flourished (cf. Bristol and Bordeaux) with the rise of colonial trade in the 16th and 17th centuries, but its later activities have been linked up with the coastal trade of Brittany. It has ship-building yards and metallurgical industries originally dependent on local ores.

Modern conditions of transport have necessitated the construction of the outport of St. Nazaire, sheltered behind the northern lip of the estuary. It competes with Bordeaux and Le Havre for American trade, and has large smelting works and ship-building yards. But both Nantes and St. Nazaire are also ports for the hinterland of south Armorica, with which they are so intimately connected by nature, and St. Nazaire has important oil-refineries.

Chapter 15

ALSACE-LORRAINE

1 *Definitions*

Alsace-Lorraine may be said to balance Armorica on the other side of the Paris basin. It stands out towards the Rhine, between the Alps and the Ardennes, much as Armorica projects into the sea between the Bay of Biscay and the English Channel. The one region is continental in its affinities, the other oceanic. Both regions have, in parts, a language other than French, and both were late in joining the French kingdom.

This area has been thrice invaded by Germany within a century and was part of the German Empire between 1871 and the 1914–18 war—though about two-thirds of Lorraine remained in French hands—and again in 1940–45. Now the French frontier is restored to its former position along the Rhine in Alsace.

The whole region is, geographically and historically, one of transition. Routes of prehistoric antiquity cross from north to south and from east to west, but they find no common centre here. Strasbourg ("city of roads") is a great nodal point, it is true, but its position is not central enough to serve the whole region, and Lorraine has never had one centre clearly dominating the others. Topographically Alsace is utterly different from Lorraine, yet when we think of the region as a whole in relation to other regions round about, a distinctive personality emerges. The use of a term such as "north-eastern France" would seem to deny it this personality, so that we have kept the historian's label, although it is a name which is not used in the region itself.

2 *Physical Characters*

Lorraine may be defined as the hill-country east of Champagne, Alsace as the eastern edge of that hill-country and the

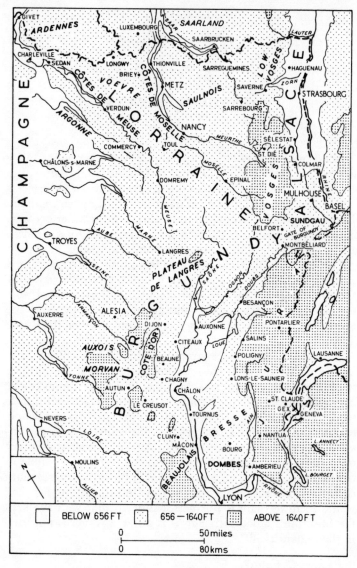

Figure 18 Alsace-Lorraine and Burgundy

long rift-valley which lies between it and the Rhine. The Vosges, one of the corner-stones of France, are common to both, and with them our description may conveniently begin. They form the geological core and the drainage centre of the whole region. Around their gentle western flanks lie the sedimentary rocks of Lorraine: under their faulted eastern scarp is the rift-valley of Alsace. The dividing line between French and German speech roughly follows the watershed.

Archaean schists, granite and palaeozoic formations outcrop in the Vosges, the granite rising in smooth-topped domes ("ballons") to over 4,500 feet in the south, where the effect of Alpine stresses was naturally most marked. Across the Rhine, the Black Forest repeats these geological and topographical features, and between them a great depth (600 feet) of later deposits has accumulated to form the plain of Alsace, falling from a height of 800 feet above sea in the south to 300 in the north.

Opposite Strasbourg the Vosges change character, and north of the Saverne (Zabern) Gap they become the Low (or Sandstone) Vosges. Here the crystalline core is buried under Triassic sandstones, cut into tabular blocks by rivers. The Low Vosges, though only about 1,500 feet in height, show the same tilt up to the east as the High Vosges, and have always formed a barrier between Alsace and Lorraine. The same belt of sandstones is wrapped around the western flanks of the High Vosges, and is followed by successively younger strips of clays and limestones as far as the Côtes de Meuse, overlooking the eastern edge of the Paris basin.

This region of alternating clays and limestones, worn by river action into narrow vales and scarped ridges, is the heart of Lorraine. The ridges are the most striking feature of the landscape. They may be compared with the escarpments of the Paris basin and they are, in fact, structurally similar to those outcrops, but the relief, the sharp profiles and the drainage pattern all serve to distinguish Lorraine from the region to the west.

The original streams were "consequent" in type, following

the dip-slope of the strata westwards from the Vosges. "Subsequent" [1] valleys developed later, and, working along the clay beds, carried the drainage northwards under the edges of the resistant limestone exposures. Thus were formed the Meuse and the Moselle, taking nearly all the waters of Lorraine northwards to join the Rhine. Highly important are the notches, formerly occupied by consequent streams, cut in the ridges. These gaps have offered strategic sites for towns at their entrances: notably Toul commands the ancient passage through which the upper Moselle once joined the Meuse. Though the general slope of the region is northwards and westwards from the Vosges, the ridges may reach heights of well over 1,000 feet even in the north-west (Côtes de Meuse).

The surface of the Alsatian plain, while generally level, is diversified by stony accumulations under the Vosges, and by broad stretches of loess above the river flats and gravel terraces. It is not the Rhine but the Ill that forms the real artery of this southern part of the plain, which is Upper Alsace. Only through Strasbourg does the life of the region touch the Rhine, which thus keeps something of its character as a frontier. The Ill, flowing for 80 miles parallel to the main river, takes its rise under the Jura in the Sundgau, a high alluvial terrace (1,000 feet) related to the former drainage of the upper Rhine into the Saône basin by the Gate of Belfort. North of Strasbourg the western tributaries flow independently to the Rhine. The first and most important of these is the Zorn, which opens a way towards Lorraine by the Saverne Gap, the lowest col in the Vosges.

There is a good deal of variety in the climates of different parts of the region. In Lorraine, the Côtes have twice as much rain as the Paris area and the winters are colder and set in earlier. Alsace, in the shelter of the Vosges, has a light rainfall: the summer maximum reveals a climate now definitely continental. There is much less cloud than in Lorraine, and more sun. Rain is very heavy on the high windward slopes of the

---

[1] "Subsequent" streams are longitudinal drainage lines so called because they develop later than the "consequent" streams which follow the direction of the slope.

Vosges but diminishes rapidly on the Alsatian side. Snow may linger for nearly half the year on the summits.

In Lorraine and on both sides of the Vosges, forest still clothes most of the higher ground, though the woods were badly mutilated in the two world wars. Spruce and beech climb to 4,000 feet in the Vosges, but the summits have kept their moors and open pastures, while clearings are common below about 2,500 feet. Lower down towards the Alsatian plain there are woods of chestnut and of walnut.

The agricultural vales of Lorraine have been cleared of their natural forest, and this sharpens the contrast with the steep ridges in between. Many local names for little natural regions once isolated by forest illustrate the rich diversity behind the historic individuality of Lorraine. The loess of Alsace, probably never heavily forested, has for ages been open cultivated land, but towards the Rhine extensive patches of forest remain both on the marshes and on the gravel belts.

3 *Lorraine*

In modern times the economic importance of Lorraine lies in her mineral wealth, which includes salt, iron and coal. Saulnois, part of the plateau between the rivers Moselle and Sarre, derives its name from salt deposits which have been utilized since the earliest Iron Age. Iron working, with the aid of charcoal, is also long-established about Nancy, immediately to the south-west of Saulnois, but the scattered ores formerly used differ from the famous *minette*[1] worked today.

Local paper, textile and glass industries were found here and there, too, but until 1870–80 Lorraine remained almost entirely agricultural.

The clay plateau of which the Saulnois is part provides rich pasture and despite its elevation (1,000 feet) grows cereals and sugar-beet. Under the Côtes de Moselle the belt of Liassic soils along the river is richly cultivated and the sunny limy slopes around Metz have long grown the vine and other fruits.

---

[1] *Minette:* the name given to the phosphoric ores of Lorraine. They are characterized by an oolitic (small-grained) structure and contain from 25–40 per cent of iron.

Between the Moselle and the Meuse stiff clays recur in Woëvre: the surface is dotted with lakes and woods, but fine wheat crops are produced.

The Meuse cuts a narrow valley between its Côtes, and here the old life of the country goes on in little towns like Commercy. But the main settlements in this frontier region tend to be strategic, and Verdun had tragic prominence during the war of 1914–18. This town illustrates the way in which the more important centres are related to cross routes between the Paris Basin and the Rhine, making use of the water-worn breaches in the Côtes. The Roman road from Reims to Strasbourg passed through Verdun and Metz. Toul lay on an alternative route farther south and from it a road went south to Langres and the Saône. Toul, Metz and Verdun kept up their prestige through the church and long retained their independence as ecclesiastical lordships (Les Trois Evêchés). The cross-routes were much used in the days of the Champagne Fairs. Vidal de la Blache draws attention to the cult of St. Rémy (the patron saint of Reims) which left many dedications to the saint in the Meuse region: cf. Domrémy, birthplace of St. Joan.

Before it leaves Lorraine to cut its narrow winding gorge through the Ardennes, the Meuse widens its valley near the little town of Sedan, the centre of an old woollen industry. Here, too, about Charleville and Mézières, modern metallurgical works use coal from Belgium and iron-ore brought down the canalized Meuse. A curious strategic loop of French territory runs down the river as far as Givet.

Many political and industrial problems have turned about the Saar coal-field, most of which lies in what is now Saarland. The river Sarre (Saar) rises towards the north of the High Vosges, and is crossed, at or near Sarrebourg, by the road, railway and canal coming through the Saverne Gap. Turning to the north-west near Sarreguemines (Saargemünd) the river enters the coal-field at Saarbrücken and continues across it to join the Moselle not far from Trèves. There are some mines on the French side of the frontier, and the coal-field actually extends south-west to the Moselle along Hercynian trend-lines.

The Saar Territory was created under the terms of the

Treaty of Versailles to enable France to work the coal in compensation for the destruction of her mines in the north. The Territory became an autonomous state, though the French government controlled the working of the mines. In 1935 a plebiscite was held under the terms of the treaty, and the people of the Saar voted for their return to German rule. Ten years later it became part of the French zone of occupation and in 1947 it was accorded international status inside an economic union with France. Finally, in 1957, it reverted to Germany as one of the lands (Saarland) of the Federal Republic, remaining in the customs zone of France, however, until the end of 1959.

Saar coals now produce coke suitable for modern blast furnaces, and iron and steel works dependent on Lorraine ores have grown up in Saarland and adjacent areas.

The minette ore of Lorraine underlies the Oolitic limestone of the Côtes de Moselle and of the plateau between the Moselle and the Meuse. The ores crop out along the valley sides and can be worked from *adits*[1] in most places: the main fields are those of Nancy, Longwy and Metz-Thionville. The full story of the Lorraine iron-ores is a long one, complicated by the rivalry of France and Germany. In 1871 the frontier was fixed so as to include in Germany the Metz-Thionville field, the only one then worked. The French subsequently developed, with the help of workers who had withdrawn from the annexed territories, a group of varied industries around Nancy and with the discovery of ores in the neighbourhood large-scale exploitation began (1880–90). Today, with the Metz fields restored, France ranks fifth among the countries of the world, and not far behind Great Britain, as a producer of steel. It is interesting to notice that the discovery of the French ores synchronized with the appearance of the Gilchrist-Thomas process of smelting (1878). The phosphoric content of the ores makes the utilization of this method necessary.

The major difficulty has been the necessity to import coke. The principal steel-producing countries of Western Europe lie so close to the bitterly disputed frontier of Western Germany

[1] *Adits* are horizontal tunnels.

that their co-operation has been bedevilled by politics (see p. 183, however, for international agreements reached since 1953).

The historic city of Nancy (Pl. VI) is the centre of the metallurgical industry, but it also has textile, glass, leather and chemical works, based to some extent on local supplies, e.g., of sand and salt. After 1918, when the frontier returned to the Rhine, the population of Nancy dropped from 120,000 to 108,000, but by 1962 it had increased to 129,000.

Lorraine has another industrial area in the valleys under the High Vosges. Small specialized manufactures (glass, paper, embroidery) are of old standing here, but the modern textile industry has grown out of calico-printing introduced in the 18th century. The spinning of cotton followed, spreading as a cottage industry especially in the valleys on the Alsatian slope. After the Franco-Prussian War of 1870–71, many cotton mills moved into Lorraine and towns like Épinal and St. Dié, using the water-power of the upper Moselle and Meurthe, grew rapidly. Coal is now imported along these valley-routes, and all branches of the industry have been maintained under the Vosges despite the distance from coal.

4 Alsace

Alsace resembles Lorraine in that it falls into strips of country running north and south, some attracting and some repelling settlement; but in nearly every way, as we have seen, the two regions differ.

The loess soils of the Alsatian plain, dry and fertile, have been occupied from prehistoric times. A great fan of loess to the west of Strasbourg brings that city into easy connection with the Saverne Gap, and from Roman times, at any rate, its site has been of outstanding importance. Similarly the break between the Vosges and the Jura—the Gate of Belfort—has made the high terraces of the Sundgau ("the South Country") a meeting-place of ways from early times.

At right angles to these cross-ways is the main avenue of Alsace, part of a great natural thoroughfare between the Alps and the North Sea. If we remember, further, the dry sunny climate, the cornfields, vineyards and orchards of an open land surrounded by wet forested hills, we shall understand the physical attractions of Alsace.

But this wealthy meeting-place of men lies along one of the great frontier lines of Europe, a line fixed nearly 2,000 years ago as the boundary between the Roman and the non-Roman worlds. The barbarian invasions carried Alemannic dialects west of the Rhine, and they have been retained by the peasantry of Alsace as far west as the Vosges watershed and Saverne. But the cities and the upper middle classes of Alsace have, since the 16th century, felt their links with France. In the 18th century this part of France was given special treatment as a frontier province; and the French Revolution did much to make the Rhine a "spiritual frontier".

Industries were developing when the Germans gained possession in 1870. Since 1919, with Alsace again in French hands,[1] Paris has been anxious to make the region more fully a part of the French nation, and the effects of this policy remain to be seen. In religion and language and to some extent in political sympathies there are divergences which add to the problems of government.

The valleys of the Vosges, using water-power, combine dairy farming with textile industries, which are connected economically with the textile centres on the Lorraine side. Roads and railways have been driven over the cols, e.g., from Strasbourg to St. Dié. Sawmills and pulp works depend on the abundant pine woods and the swift streams.

Below, in the valley of the Ill, Mulhouse and Colmar have developed as industrial centres. Mulhouse stands on the edges of the Sundgau, where the vine grows well on limy slopes. Factors of communication which gave its site strategic value have also affected its economic life. It is the centre of the Alsatian textile industries, coal being easily brought by the Rhine-Rhône canal. Adjoining the town are large potash beds on which dyeing and chemical works depend. Colmar deals with artificial silk as well as with woollens and cottons. A few miles farther north is Sélestat, beyond which the chief loess

[1] Alsace became the German "Westmark" between 1940 and 1945.

areas occur in the widening plains between the Ill and the Vosges.

Under the whole length of the hills vineyards flourish on the dry soils: here and there a vintage of special renown (e.g., Gertwiller, Ribeauville, Molsheim) is produced. On the lower terraces of the valley-floor the main crops are cereals, fruit, and, north of Strasbourg, hops and tobacco. The German frontier is reached where the river Lauter flows across the valley between the forested belts of Bien and Hagenau.

Strasbourg, like all the other Alsatian towns, is not on the Rhine, and though its canal connections are being rapidly improved, it still owes more to its roads and railways than to the river. The Rhine, in this part of its course an international river, yet keeps some of the characters of an Alpine stream. Its broad swift current is split up into innumerable channels, and swamp-forest still covers the banks and islands in many places. The main channel is regularized, but this process has shortened the course of the river and so stiffened its gradient. Winter ice and summer floods are serious hindrances to navigation.

Strasbourg is thus the effective head of economic river transport; and it is here that the Rhine-Rhône and Rhine-Marne canals meet. The French have constructed new docks on the south side of the town in anticipation of the completion of the Rhine lateral canal. The first section of this has been built in connection with the great barrage at Kembs, near Basel. The hydro-electric station was completed in 1933 and with other Rhine installations serves much of east France as far as Troyes. Alongside the barrage are locks totalling 130 feet in depth, and the scheme has the effect of raising the level of the Rhine to allow traffic up to Basel.

Strasbourg was utilized by Germany in the 1914–18 war for coking Ruhr coal and shipping Moselle ores to Westphalia. Coking activities continue and the town has also attracted engineering works. It promises to develop as the economic centre of much of Lorraine as well as of Alsace, and will help to weld together these two provinces, so long divergent in their main interests. It has important oil-refineries. Its population had reached 229,000 in 1962.

Chapter 16

BURGUNDY

1 *A Transition Region*

We may think of Burgundy as embracing the upper valley
of the Saône and its marginal hills—the Jura on one side and
the Côte d'Or and Plateau de Langres on the other. Politically
the word Burgundy has had various meanings. The boundaries
of the old province of that name were fluctuating and uncer-
tain, but the nucleus of the region lay along the south-eastern
edge of the limestone hills of the Côte d'Or department, about
Dijon. The rulers of Burgundy owed their power to their control of the passes through those hills, leading towards Lorraine,
Champagne and Flanders, but especially towards Paris.

To the east of Dijon is the Gate of Belfort (or Burgundy)
and due south the corridor of the lower Saône and Rhône. To
the west, the Morvan hills would seem to block the way, yet
the limestones round about it have carried lines of movement
and of expansion in this direction; and Burgundy long included
part of the upper Loire basin. The Morvan, moreover, is isolated from the Central Plateau by a zone of weak relief about
Autun and Le Creusot. In the south-east are the long parallel
ridges of the Jura, followed for most of their length by the
Swiss frontier, but crossed, near Pontarlier, by one of the great
thoroughfares of modern Europe, the shortest route from the
Straits of Dover to the Alpine passes and Italy.

Thus Burgundy lies open in all directions, and influences
from all sides have moulded its life. But the ambitious aims of
Charles the Bold, the last duke, to revive and extend the power
of Burgundy from Provence to the Low Countries, while appro-
priate to the position of the Duchy, were doomed to failure
because of the lack of a territorial base in proportion to the
extent of the region. The Saône valley of itself has not had the
means to produce a political centre of gravity: the true rôle

of Burgundy has been that of connecting link between the Seine and Rhône basins (Fig. 18).

Structurally, the region is clearly defined by the relations between old blocks and new folds. The Jura folds, gently curving between the Rhône and the Rhine, are pinched and restricted towards those rivers as they face the northern end of the Central Plateau and the southern end of the Vosges. The trough is 150 miles in length, narrowing to about 15 miles in the Gate of Burgundy and reaching its greatest width (about 45 miles) between Salins and Dijon. The drainage of this trough, which was once a lake (Lac de Bresse), converges upon a depression of which Châlon now marks the centre. The basin is floored with sands and clays.

The Saône rises on the Seuil de Lorraine west of the southern Vosges; the headwaters of the Meuse and Moselle are nearby and Burgundy passes without break into Lorraine. From the south end of the Vosges the Ognon flows south-westwards along a line of faults. The Gate of Burgundy is drained by tributaries of the Doubs, which, rising in the Jura far to the south-west and once flowing on to the Rhine, alternately cuts across and follows ridge and furrow until it emerges and flows back to join the Saône in the Châlon depression. The Ain takes the drainage of the southern Jura directly to the Rhône.

Facing the central Jura mountains, the limestones to which they give their name (Jurassic) stand out again in the Plateau de Langres, where the Seine, Aube and Marne take their rise. These rivers open up ways guarded by such fortified settlements as Alesia (in Gallo-Roman times) and Langres. The plateau narrows southwards and passes into the Côte d'Or (2,000 feet) whose long straight scarp between Dijon and Chagny overlooks the Saône flowing parallel to it some 15 miles away. The slopes between the hills and the river are the great wine districts of Burgundy, and here, too, both the political and the old religious centres of the region are to be found, e.g., Citeaux: see p. 128.

The Morvan, lying to the west of the Côte d'Or, is a distinctive land of forests, bogs and streaming waters, rising to 3,000 feet. The Yonne and its tributaries flow north towards

the Seine, among them the river Armançon, which, north-east
of the Morvan, brings the Paris basin into close contact with
Burgundy through the border *pays* of Auxois.

At Châlon, the Saône turns southwards and follows close
under the edge of the plateau, leaving a rectangular strip of
lowland between it and the southern Jura. This is Bresse,
fat pasture land traversed by routes from Mâcon to Bourg
which cross the Jura into Savoy. These routes avoid the
Pays de Dombes, a land of moraines and meres extending
nearly to Lyon, and forming the southern end of the Saône
basin.

2 *The Saône*

The Sâone valley has a climate marked by a considerable
range of temperature and a fairly heavy rainfall. The rain is
heaviest on the higher parts and lightest in the lee of the
Morvan and Côte d'Or heights, around Dijon and Beaune.
Winter is fairly dry in the lowlands and most rain falls in early
summer, with a second maximum in autumn.

In early days, while woods and swamps covered the floor of
the Saône basin and must have blocked the Gate of Burgundy,
the adjoining Jurassic belt was dry and less encumbered with
forest, and thus it formed the prehistoric routeway from Central Europe. The Jura had the attraction, also, of salt, which
was much sought after when agriculture and industry expanded in the late Bronze Age. In the early days of iron,
sword-using warriors pushed west along the Jura and reached
the Plateau de Langres and Berry. Soon afterwards, if not
before, ways were opened northwards from the Rhône, and
these, crossing the lines that led from east to west, made the
Côte d'Or region the meeting-place of routes it has been ever
since.

In Roman times, three cities—Autun, Langres, Besançon—
gathered up the roads that met at Châlon to follow the rivers
to Lyon and Arles. The Burgundians came in from the east
before the fall of the Empire and became rulers of Savoy,
later extending their territory to the Loire. In 843 the region
became part of Lotharingia, and emerged as a feudal state

ultimately to be incorporated, after long struggles, in the French kingdom. During the Middle Ages, Burgundy controlled the trade-routes from the south to the Champagne fairs, and became a focus of thought and a great centre of monastic organization. Cluny and Cîteaux (whence came the Cistercian order) were real capitals of Christendom: they lie on little tributaries of the Saône draining from the Côte d'Or and the Beaujolais hills. In the crusades and the pilgrim movement Burgundy was a notably active centre, and it was the home of an important school of Romanesque architecture. At Dijon the visitor can see, in the works of Carl Sluter, the remarkable advances made in free sculpture by the late 14th century. During the 15th century the region began to profit from the revival of trade and civilization in the Renaissance, and we have referred above to the attempt of Charles the Bold to restore the ancient kingdom.

Though politically Burgundy had to give way to the centralized power of the Paris basin, it keeps something of its historic individuality. Its fame as a meeting-place must endure; indeed Dijon is one of the busiest railway junctions in France. The lower slopes of the Côte d'Or between Dijon and Chagny are clothed with vineyards that produce the best Burgundy wines—Garey, Beaune, Meursault. Villages and towns are placed where streams issue from the escarpment, and the population is dense. Dijon deals with the marketing of the wines and it has doubled in size within the last half-century. The railway to Paris tunnels under the scarp of the Plateau de Langres and joins a tributary valley of the Armançon at Alise Ste. Reine, the successor of the Gaulish Alesia.

On the plateau-top the rainfall is heavy and woodland abundant, and agriculture gives way to sheep and cattle rearing. Langres is a strongly fortified town which looks to Dijon as its capital although it lies near the source of the Marne. The Morvan marks the western limit of Burgundy: it is a region apart, avoided by the movements of man, a region of cold impoverished soils, scattered farms and much woodland. It has had the effect of deflecting lines of communication, and the Roman Autun remains an important road centre on its eastern flank.

The lowlands of the Saône, sometimes referred to as the Plain of Burgundy, form rich agricultural land bearing crops of wheat and maize. Stretches of sandy deposits are forested, and woods share with rank pastures the alluvial flood-plain where the broad river winds among willows and poplars. Villages lie thick in the plain, but they approach the river only where natural terraces give protection from floods. Here and there towns have grown up at the crossing-places—Auxonne, Châlon, Tournus, Mâcon—but none of these can compare with Dijon or with Besançon. Conditions did not favour the rise of a political centre on the river.

In the Gate of Burgundy a low limestone plateau runs out from the Jura towards the Vosges, where the Ballon d'Alsace rises abruptly to 4,100 feet. Alluvial deposits washed down from this steep face occupy the northern part of the gap: their lake-strewn surface contrasts sharply with the red limestone *buttes*, such as that which has made Belfort a strong fortress since the Middle Ages. Today, with the frontier at the Rhine, Belfort has lost its strategic value, but it is expanding as an industrial centre, though the population (48,000) has fallen since 1880, when it was 68,000. The town is admirably placed at the point of convergence of routes by road, rail and canal. Specializing in electrical engineering, it is closely linked economically with Mulhouse on the one hand and Besançon on the other.

3 The Jura

The Jura mountains form one of the most distinctive structural elements of France. Fully 150 miles in length, they are characterized throughout by the regular arrangement of parallel ridges and valleys corresponding to folded anticline and syncline.[1] The synclinal troughs are connected one with another by deep transverse gorges (*cluses*) that are highly characteristic. The alternating ridges and valleys are known as *monts* and *vals*. Normally two structural belts can be recognized: an outer plateau zone (1,500–2,500 feet) dropping in a series of terraces

[1] The names given by geologists to up-folds (anticlines) and down-folds (synclines).

to the Saône basin and intensely faulted, and an inner folded zone, reaching its maximum intensity and height in the Hautes Chaînes (4,500 feet) which overlook the Swiss lakes in a long line between the upper Rhône and the upper Rhine. The two belts are not everywhere equally developed, and the whole may most conveniently be described in three sections.

NORTHERN JURA Here the Swiss frontier follows the Doubs and leaves only the plateau to France, but the Lomont ridge divides a higher plateau to the south from a lower and more fertile stretch to the north. Montbéliard is the centre of an industrial area, long concerned with weaving and iron-working, which expanded with the annexation of Alsace by the Germans (cf. Épinal and Belfort), and now carries on watch-making, spinning and cycle and motor manufactures. Local water-power is largely employed, but the area has been drawn into the wider industrial region that includes Besançon, Belfort and Mulhouse. The Pays de Montbéliard retained its inde-pendence until late in the 18th century, when it became part of France.

CENTRAL JURA The middle section of the Jura is the broadest. From Besançon to Bourg the plateau rises steeply to an average height of 1,000 feet above the plains, road and railway running parallel underneath. The long scarp is an area of broken relief where favourable exposures have the vine (les Vignobles) and where salt deposits brought early settlement (cf. the place-names Salins and Lons-le-Saunier). Here and there, streams have isolated spurs which offered defensive sites for towns profiting from the interchange of products between plateau and plain.

Besançon, in a remarkable loop of the Doubs, guards the approach from the Gate of Burgundy under the plateau. It is the headquarters of the watch-making industry, introduced from Switzerland in the 18th century. The influence of Alsace is seen in its textile industries, and there are also steel and motor-car works. Besançon had the first factory in Europe for the making of artificial silk, from the forests of the Jura. Like Belfort, it has owed much of its economic development to its relations with Upper Alsace. All along the edge of the plateau a dense population bears witness to the prosperity of a *piedmont* (hill-foot) belt.

The table-land itself is very different. The landscape takes on *karstic* (causse-like) features: there are few water-courses and the climate is one of extremes. Only rarely, where erosion has revealed the underlying marls or where the Alpine glaciers have left morainic deposits, do we find meadows and plough-lands. The Loue, rising near Pontarlier, cuts a deep valley as it flows out to join the Doubs, and here forests of oak and beech give way lower down to fruit orchards and fields of maize and wheat. But the plateau is thinly peopled and relatively barren.

In the folded Jura, woods of spruce make their appearance and the green *vals* have stock-raising and dairying, which are combined with forestry. Many small domestic industries, often using water-power for lathes, are found, and articles in wood or horn are made, with characteristic peasant patience, in the long leisure of winter. Watch-making has been readily taken up by a people thus trained in skilled handicrafts. The railway from Lausanne to Pontarlier and Dijon crosses the Jura in this section, and has no doubt helped to contribute to its more recent prosperity. A centre of special activity is found about St. Claude, where the southern Jura begin. Briar pipes, origin-ally made from local box, are a widely-known product, and an adaptable people turns easily to making plastic gadgets or the latest toys that fashion decrees. Other articles produced are optical glasses, jewellery and scientific instruments.

SOUTHERN JURA West of Lake Geneva the Jura, now directly facing the granites of Beaujolais, gradually change their direc-tion and run almost due south. With this change the distinc-tion between plateau and folds disappears: the whole system is intensely folded and the width correspondingly reduced. At the southern extremity of the range the folds overlap each other and the Rhône is driven farther and farther south to find an outlet to the west. Much morainic material testifies to the extension of Alpine glaciation in Pleistocene times.

All this section of the Jura is in France, which also pushes a tiny wedge on to the Swiss plateau towards Geneva (the pays de Gex). There is now a clear distinction between the ridges and the valleys. The former have pastures and pine forests with naked limestone showing through; the climate is hard and snow lies for many months of the year. But the forests yield high returns because they are near the busy valleys, where apples and grapes ripen in the strong sun, and the population is denser than anywhere else in the Jura. Water-power is utilized for many local industries, and the influence of Lyon has brought silk spinning and weaving to towns like Nantua, on the railway from Bourg to Geneva. Ambérieu occupies a similar position on the line from Lyon to Geneva, making use of the transverse *cluses*. Hereabouts we pass on the one hand into the region of Lyon and the Rhône valley, and on the other into the French Alps.

Chapter 17

THE CENTRAL PLATEAU

1 *General Features*

The Central Plateau is a block of irregular upland, averaging 3,000 feet in height, placed centrally in the southern half of France. Its limits are marked in a general way by the 1,000 feet contour. It owes its relief to the uplift occasioned by the Alpine stresses, and to the eruptive rocks that poured through vents along dislocations formed at that time.

The volcanic *puys* (up to 6,188 feet in Mt. Dore) are its highest points. The heights of Auvergne, including Mt. Dore and the great Puy de Dôme overlooking Clermont Ferrand, run north and south alongside the upper Allier. Southwards lies the enormous spreading cone of the Cantal, and from here the volcanic rocks stretch south-east in the Monts d'Aubrac. Eruptive sheets also occupy wide areas in the mountains of Velay in Haute Loire. But the general slope of the plateau is to the north and west, towards the basins of Paris and Aquitaine, and topographically its greatest unifying feature is the long high ridge of the Cévennes, steeply faulted towards the Rhône and the Mediterranean.

Internally, faulting along north-south lines brought further diversity by causing the subsidence of crustal blocks. The upper Loire and Allier make use of these basins in escaping from the plateau. On the west, the Tarn, Aveyron, Lot and Dordogne have cut cliff-edged valleys or great gorges through the uplifted rocks. The underlying Hercynian structure-lines, though disguised by later complications, remain important in that they determine the location of several small coal-fields, as we saw in Chapter 2.

Extensive upland areas tend as a rule to have climatic characteristics of their own, and the Central Plateau is large enough and high enough to make its own climate. It also plays a significant rôle in separating Atlantic conditions from those of the Mediterranean. Rainfall is heaviest on high slopes facing north and west. Aspect is important too for temperature, which is often mild on south-facing slopes while winter on the heights

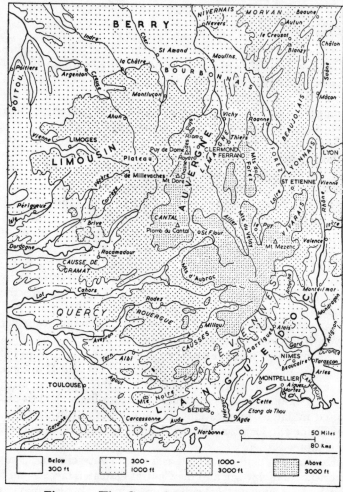

Figure 19 The Central Plateau and Languedoc

is bleak and snowy. Deep-sunk valleys, however, suffer from
the creep of dense cold air from the uplands. In summer the
hottest areas are the enclosed basins drained by the Allier and
Loire, where too the winters are cold and the rainfall low.
Taking the plateau as a whole, if spring tends to be late,
autumn is also late and allows grapes and other fruits to ripen
in many places.

Natural pasture is abundant on the granitic and volcanic
watersheds, richer on the latter rocks, poorer and often passing
into heath on the former. Lower down, the slopes were formerly
densely wooded with oak, ash, beech and chestnut, but long
human occupation has resulted in the clearing of much of this
forest, except on the wettest hills. The chestnut woods used to
provide a source of food for both men and animals: they remain characteristic of the Cévennes up to 2,500 feet, but have
been much ravaged by disease. Here and in the Vivarais and
Limousin, the belt of chestnut forests corresponds to a zone of
relatively dense peopling. Hardy cereals, barley and rye, are
characteristic of the uplands; and buckwheat, a plant of oceanic
climate, is grown along the milder western margins. In the
limestone *causses*, the dry soil is often bare. There are scanty
stretches of sweet grass, box and scattered thorns, but woodland is absent save for pine-woods, mostly recent plantations.

2 *Human Characteristics*

The Central Plateau, with its irregular relief and divergent
drainage lines, has never been a unit historically. No centre
of organization has had the strength to impose unity where
communications are so difficult and conditions of life so varied.
The historic life of the plateau has developed around a number of local gathering-points, often placed near the edges where
upland and lowland meet. In the same way, parts of these two
contrasted zones—hill and plain—have often been combined
in political units such as Bourbonnais and Beaujolais.

But the upland-dwellers are conscious of the differences of
life and thought which divide them from the plainsmen, on
whom they "look down". The habit of independent thought
led them to rebel against the Roman church in the Albigensian

movement, and there were also many Huguenot strongholds here. In the southern valleys, the Protestant church has many supporters today.

Such human tendencies, together with obvious individuality of environment, have helped to keep the plateau a region apart, but the most potent force has been the difficulty of communications. Between east and west, between the Rhône basin and Aquitaine, the plateau imposes a serious barrier. Movements north from the Mediterranean have had to turn its flanks; even the Roman power did not penetrate from this side. Only on the north and north-east are there easy ways in, and the organized strength of the Paris basin made itself felt here. If, thanks to the open valleys in the north, the north-south lines of communication are less difficult than those from east to west, it nevertheless takes twice as long to travel by train from Paris to Marseille by way of Clermont-Ferrand as by the rather longer Dijon route.

It must be remembered, however, that the region belongs to the Midi in its language and civilization as well as in its latitude. And it has helped to spread the culture of the south, bringing mountain energy, individuality and perseverance to strengthen the more precocious advances along the lowland routes. It has made many contributions, thanks to the emigrants it must send out, to the general life of France.

3 *Limousin and Auvergne*

The divisions of the plateau are still distinguished, as is often the case in France, by names of ancient lineage. Certain tracts have been inhabited continuously since the passing of the ice-sheets, and the adaptation of man to the soil is correspondingly intimate.

We may begin our description with one of the simplest regions—Limousin—the north-western shoulder of the plateau. The land sinks gently from the Cantal towards the Gate of Poitou along the Hercynian axis, but at any point the uplands form a nearly level surface, deeply dissected by active streams of which the Vienne is the chief. Most of the area is divided into small hedge-lined fields, and there are chestnut plantations, for timber and fruit, on the valley slopes, and water-meadows along the rivers. Horses, cattle and poultry are its main products.

But Limousin has another side to its character thanks to its famous capital city, Limoges. The Roman *Augustoritum* took its name from the passage (*ritum* = a ford) over the Vienne, where routes from the north and the east, turning the shoulder of the plateau to reach the south-west, crossed the river. Its nodality brought many influences from the larger world outside. Limoges became a great Christian centre and place of pilgrimage, and trading colonies (e.g., of Venetians) were established there. Its artistic fame is centred about its ancient enamel manufacture, but it also has renown for its troubadour literature and for its Romanesque buildings.

The town declined as the Paris basin came to prominence, but it kept up a woollen industry based on supplies of clear water and rapid streams. The railways brought new possibilities of manufacture, and today the local kaolin is made into Limoges china with the aid of water-wheels and coal, some of which comes from the small field of Ahun on the Creuse. Moreover, the fairs of Limoges are widely attended and Limousin cattle have a high reputation. Other old market towns which profit from the meeting of upland and lowland are Argenton on the borders of Berry, and Brive in its fertile basin on the Corrèze to the south.

The streams which cross Limousin in a fan from the Corrèze to the Creuse take their rise in a great mass of granite that forms the highest part of the Limousin plateau. This is known as Millevaches (thousand springs), a country of high rounded summits up to 3,000 feet in height. Heavy rainfall and thin acid soils limit cultivation; the crops are rye, buckwheat and potatoes. Cattle are reared in summer on the high pastures. The population is scanty and there is much emigration to Paris.

Auvergne lies to the east of Limousin. Its main features are aligned north and south. The Allier flows through and has to the west the high volcanic country of the Auvergne mountains, narrowing and giving way, north of the 46th parallel, to the ancient rock-platform on which they rest.

The Cantal occupies the southern end of these volcanic heights. It is the remnant of an enormous cone, over 30 miles across, its sides scored with radial valleys often very fertile and warm. Between them are long triangular tracts of sloping country (*planaises*) which provide rich summer pastures in their upper levels and good wheatlands lower down, especially on the drier eastern side. Mont Dore, to the north of Cantal, is a more complex and irregular block: it has the highest summit of the whole plateau in the Puy de Sancy, over 6,000 feet. It is succeeded by the Chaîne des Puys, a striking group of cones of many types, dominated by the Puy de Dôme (4,800 feet).

The valley of the Allier broadens below the Chaîne des Puys into the level floor of a former lake, something over 1,000 feet in height. This is La Limagne, the largest of the internal basins of the plateau. A low terrace rises abruptly on the west side of the river, bounded by the steep escarpment of the crystalline platform and its volcanic load. Under this scarp many residual hills of Tertiary marls and limestone stand out, often capped by lava flows. They are a striking feature of Limagne, providing springs and defensive sites of old, their fertile sunny slopes lined with orchards and vineyards. The lowland round about is irrigated and yields rich crops of wheat and sugar-beet. Many prosperous settlements are aligned under the main escarpment, serving as market-places for the products of pastoral hills and cultivated plain. Clermont, Royat and Riom are larger towns.

Clermont-Ferrand, with a population of 128,000, is a centre for a great part of the plateau. It has long-established activities as the centre of a rich agricultural district, e.g., preserving fruit, making food-pastes and leather, while Royat is well-known as a mineral-water spa, its hot springs related to the vulcanism of Puy de Dôme. Clermont's early interest in rubber manufacture has developed into great tyre and motor-car industries. Another string of small towns occupies the eastern escarpment of Limagne (cf. Thiers). Vichy,[1] on the river lower

[1] It was the seat of the puppet government of Unoccupied France, 1940–45.

down, is renowned for its waters. Hereabouts, Auvergne passes into Bourbonnais, which occupies the north-central margins of the plateau.

The Puys give way here to a plateau of ancient rocks drained by the Sioule, a pastoral land of scattered hamlets. Local coal gave rise to the now extensive metallurgical industries of Montluçon (55,000). The Cher leaves the plateau to enter the wooded Lias vale of St. Amand (La Vallée Noire), the scene of many of George Sand's novels. The lower parts of Bourbonnais are typical *bocage* country, mainly pastoral. There were once many local forges, and much charcoal burning was carried on. Nevers, on the Loire near the junction of the Allier, retains its interest in iron-working. Moulins, to the south, is one of the market-towns that make a girdle of exchange about the plateau.

Both Bourbonnais and Auvergne served for many centuries as thoroughfares between Lyon and Limoges and between Burgundy and the south-west by way of Périgueux. In modern times, communications from the Paris basin along the Allier are far more important.

4 The North-East

The north-eastern part of the plateau comprises an area of irregular topography between the Loire and the Saône. Physical continuity is broken by lines of structural weakness and low relief running north-east–south-west along Hercynian trends. The chief of these breaks is the depression occupied by the Blanzy-Le Creusot coal-field, where road, railway and canal (Canal du Centre) reach the Saône over a watershed only a little above 1,000 feet in height. Local iron supplies, now worked out, helped to start the famous iron and steel industries of Le Creusot. Autun, which controls another transverse gap to the north, and the rugged isolated Morvan, have been mentioned in Chapter 16.

Going south we come to the heights of Beaujolais and Lyonnais, and to the Forez basin lying under their steep western edge. The Forez is a foundered area floored with Tertiary lake deposits, its level terraces inadequately drained by the Loire which flows through in an entrenched course. The river next passes through a deep gorge to another large basin, the Roannais. Roanne (52,000) is a textile town linked economically to Lyon and St. Etienne. The southern end of Forez adjoins St. Etienne, but this town belongs rather to the Rhône basin.

Still farther south are the volcanic block of Mézenc and the granite of Vivarais, and to the west the smallest of the foundered basins of the plateau—that of Le Puy, also drained by the Loire. The floor is much dissected by streams and broken by hard volcanic mounds. Le Puy is the market-town and old cathedral city, fantastically dominated by two volcanic "necks", the Rochers Corneille and St. Michel.

To the west again are the high lava plateaux of Velay, passing northwards into the dreary granite lands of the Monts du Forez. This is pastoral country, varied by forestry on the high slopes and by cultivation on the lower levels.

5 *Cévennes and Causses*

A more definite unity is apparent in the Cévennes, the name given to the south-eastern edge of the plateau. Erosion is actively sculpturing its steep face, but immediately behind are the level or rolling surfaces of the ancient peneplain, with open pasture, bracken, bog or heather. There is a sudden contrast between this wet moorland landscape and the parched plains from 3,000 to 5,000 feet below: a fully Mediterranean country-side is visible only a few miles away.

The ridges which erosion has left standing out from the watershed are known as *serres*. Zones of vegetation can be traced up-hill from the vine and olive country of the limestone foothills, and midway comes the belt of chestnut forests—perhaps the most characteristic feature of the Cévennes. The mountain-dwellers, isolated in deep valleys, live a hard life and have kept independence of thought. But the population is declining here as in so many parts of rural France. The open moors above are tenanted by sheep and goats, and the herdsmen obstinately oppose schemes of reafforestation. Huge flocks of sheep are driven up to the pastures in early summer from the plains, following ancient tracks known as *drailles*. Market centres have grown up at the mouth of each valley, and of these Alais is in many ways outstanding. It has coal and blast furnaces, and through it passes the railway from Nîmes that winds over the Cévennes towards Clermont-Ferrand.

The south-western part of the plateau remains to be described. It contains the two *causse* regions of France, and between them the southernmost extension of the archaean table-land. This consists of the plateau of Rouergue, crossed by the Tarn which leaves it above Albi, and the fault-limited Montagne-Noire, darkened by chestnut forests on its northern slopes. The latter separates Aquitaine from Languedoc, and compares with the Morvan in being an outpost of the plateau set among richer lowlands. Between these crystalline areas and that of the Cévennes lie the Great Causses of Gévaudan and Larzac, through which the Tarn flows (Pl. VII) in a great gorge, 1,500 feet deep, to open out again at Millau, the capital of the Causses. Millau makes gloves and spins wool, for the limestone is sheep country. Roquefort cheese is a Causse product, and fruit growing is carried on here and there, but much of the surface is stony desert.

Nature is softer in the Little Causses of Quercy, which occupy a bay in the crystalline rocks of the plateau between the rivers Vézère and Aveyron. The limestone stands at about 1,000 feet, and although its surface is arid it will grow wheat and it is broken by cliff-edged valleys a mile or more in width, whose terraced slopes produce varied fruits that give a fore-taste of Aquitaine. The valleys of the Dordogne and Lot, its chief rivers, contain most of the population. Cahors, with its ancient bridge over the Lot, is the main town (Pl. VII), and the old sanctuary of Rocamadour is worth noting for its cliff-site and for its association with the mediaeval pilgrim ways. All this limestone region is stamped with a prehistoric antiquity. Its caves and rock shelters have played a leading part in elucidating the early cultures of western Europe.

Descendants of the old hunting peoples are still found among the present inhabitants, and a strong conservatism has its roots very deep in the past. It is a region of many survivals and its interests and activities remain almost entirely agricultural.

Chapter 18

THE BASIN OF AQUITAINE

I *A Triangle of Lowlands*

In its relief, structure and shape, the basin of Aquitaine is the simplest of the major regions of France. Its triangle of lowlands is limited by the Pyrenees, the dune-coast of the Landes and the edge of the Central Plateau. Three influences have dominated its life: the Pyrenees, the Atlantic and the plateau; but to these we must add contacts with the adjoining lowlands of the Paris basin and Languedoc by way of the Gates of Poitou and Carcassonne.

Upper Tertiary rocks occupy a much larger area in Aquitaine than anywhere else in France. Most characteristic are the *molasses*—soft limestones, sandstones and clays which give a monotonous rolling landscape to much of the Garonne basin. These loose materials were washed down from the Pyrenees, whence also were derived the vast Pleistocene detritus-fan of Lannemezan, the alluvial deposits of the Garonne, and the sands of the Landes.

Secondary rocks appear only on the north and north-east, where dislocations have allowed some of them to be incorporated in the uplifted plateau (Quercy, see p. 141). These deposits have been affected by the pressure of the folding Pyrenees pushing against the resistant axis of the Gâtine, which produced two slight parallel ridges later eroded into low plateaux. Jurassic rocks are exposed in the north, continuing through the Gate of Poitou, but the main series is of Cretaceous age. One anticline can be traced from Cognac to Périgueux and another gives the long island of Oléron its narrow hog's back.

The drainage is far simpler than that of the Paris basin. Within the triangular frame run straight river-lines. Drainage concentrates along a central line, the Garonne, which may be

143

said to bisect the apex-angle of the basin in its course from Toulouse to the Gironde. Its early tributaries are mostly Pyrenean, but lower down all its great feeders come from the

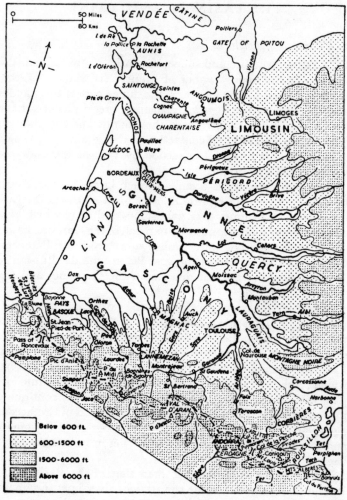

Figure 20 Aquitaine and the Pyrenees

plateau. In the north the Charente and in the south the Adour
flow independently to the Bay of Biscay.

The basin opens like a funnel, 200 miles broad at the coast,
to the moist winds of the Atlantic, yet because it is low-lying
the rainfall is not excessive. The Pyrenees act as a screen on
the south, so that only the Adour basin and the neighbouring
Landes get heavy rains (over 40 inches). Winds drawn over
the Pyrenees by cyclones to the north tend to be hot and dry
(cf. the föhn of Switzerland) and sometimes cause spring floods
by melting the mountain snows. The heaviest rain comes in
April, May and June.

Along the seaboard, however, an autumn maximum is
found. At that season, too, the heavy rains of the Cévennes
often cause flooding in the lowlands, while the valleys under
the Pyrenees are liable to sudden floods from summer thunder-
storms. The Garonne is thus subject to rapid changes of level
and flooding at most seasons. It is a formidable and even
terrifying river, and in its middle course its valley forms something of a barrier still. Between Toulouse and Bordeaux there
was no bridge over the river until the 19th century. It has
always presented serious difficulties to shipping, and the needs
of navigation have often conflicted with those of cultivation.

Aquitaine is far enough south to have hot summers, which
give way characteristically to long mild autumns. The
Atlantic ensures high humidity, gaily varied skies and mild
winters. In the extreme south-east there are sunny basins
where the climate is almost Mediterranean. Montauban
formerly grew figs, olives and almonds, but nowadays the olive
is not grown west of Carcassonne.

The south-west of France is a region of rich and varied
cultivation, and a surprising number of crops has been grown
at different times. Thanks to its transitional position between
temperate and warm-temperate latitudes it will grow cereals,
fruits and vegetables of many kinds, and its agriculture has
been called polyculture. In the 18th century, Aquitaine was
one of the most flourishing parts of France. It had important
textile industries based on locally produced wool, silk and
hemp and attempts were made to grow cotton. It specialized

in dye-crops—saffron and woad. Contacts with the New World brought maize, tobacco, beans, and later tomatoes. Of its many fruits the vine and the plum are of ancient repute; the latter is said to have come from Cyprus at the time of the Crusades.

But owing to its position and to the attraction of its soils and climate, Aquitaine knew neither peace nor prosperity until the 17th century. England maintained her hold upon it for over 300 years, valuing the possession for its wines. Long religious wars depopulated the country and interfered with its life. For centuries it lay in the track of invaders and armies coming and going along the ways from Spain. Pilgrim routes to Santiago in Galicia brought many influences from north and south. Traversed by these lines of movement and faced with internal barriers and with the double attraction of the Atlantic and Mediterranean entries, Aquitaine was never able to develop unity around a central point, but was divided between two capitals, Bordeaux and Toulouse. The latter (324,000) now exceeds Bordeaux (250,000) in size.

2 Charente and Périgord

On the north, the Charente basin gives a certain unity to the limestone lands between the Bay of Biscay and Limousin. On the river are Angoulême, Cognac, Saintes and Rochefort, and two of these towns form the centres of the pays of Angoumois and Saintonge, corresponding in a general way to the upper and lower parts of the basin.

Angoulême is a city of Roman foundation placed in a strong defensive position at a sharp bend in the river. Its 12th-century cathedral is celebrated for Byzantine cupolas which tell of long-forgotten cultural influences (cf. Périgueux, p. 147). A wide range of crops is produced on the fertile rolling country of Angoumois. The vines planted in increasing quantities along the valley slopes yield grapes that go to make brandy, and Cognac is the centre of this industry.

Saintes, a route-centre since Roman days, is the market for the cereals of Saintonge, which, stretching south to the Gironde, includes a patch of Tertiary soils as well as typical cretaceous "champagne". The estuary of the Charente is protected by the long limestone ridge of the Ile d'Oléron: Rochefort is a naval port a few miles upstream. To the north, the Ile de Ré lies opposite La Rochelle, a strongly fortified town which is now a fishing port. La Pallice has rapidly developed as out-port, and its excellent modern equipment makes it a rival to Bordeaux. The La Rochelle region (pays d'Aunis) was formerly well protected by the marshes of the river Sèvre to the north. In Roman times a sea gulf existed here, and it naturally forms the divide between the Charente country and the Vendée. North-eastwards, however, the low limestone plateaux have for centuries provided an easy way to Poitou and the Paris basin.

A broad belt of cretaceous country runs south-east from the Charente and ends against the Causses of Quercy. Its heart is Périgord, physically transitional between "champagne" and "causse", traversed by the Dordogne and its tributaries as they pass westwards from the plateau to the sea. Market-gardening, fruit-growing and the cultivation of maize occupy an inter-mediate zone between the water-meadows and the dry sheep-lands. In addition there is much forest, chiefly of chestnut and of oak, from the roots of which the renowned truffles of Péri-gord are gathered. Périgueux, the local capital, is perhaps most widely famed for its curious and very striking cathedral, surmounted by five Byzantine domes.[1] External influences such as that betrayed here have affected Périgord in the past because of its relation to the routes across and under the Central Plateau. But they have not changed to any degree the ancient and original character of its regional life.

3 The Landes and Armagnac

While Périgord is closely related to the plateau, the Landes region is naturally influenced by the Atlantic. From the Adour to the Gironde the coast is composed of a strip of sand-dunes

---

[1] Compare Angoulême and Cahors. The influence of St. Front Cathedral (Périgueux) may be seen in the Basilique du Sacré Coeur at Montmartre in Paris and in the elaborate style of the new church of Ste. Jeanne d'Arc at Nice.

some 6 miles wide and 140 miles long, broken only by the Bassin d'Arcachon where the ponded drainage breaks through to the sea. Behind the dunes a wide plain of drifted sand, carried inland by the winds, stretches to the lower Garonne and to the Adour, and so forms a broad triangle based on the Bay of Biscay. The heavy rainfall collects in wide expanses of marsh caused by the formation of an impermeable layer of iron-pan below the sandy surface.

For centuries the Landes were an inhospitable waste, sparsely peopled by shepherds inland and by fishers along the coastal lagoons—a region hostile to the movements of man. Since the 18th century, however, afforestation, drainage and the fixing of the dunes with hurdles and grasses have brought about a great change. Planted forests of maritime pine yield pit-props, railway-sleepers, telegraph-poles and paving-blocks, and the resin collected each autumn is a valuable product. Moreover cultivation is carried on in small clearings and stock is raised on the drained marshes. The population is still small, but some districts are now among the most prosperous in rural France. The risk of forest fires is minimized by the electrification of the railway from Bordeaux to Bayonne which passes through the Landes.

The influence of the Pyrenees is strongest in the region of Armagnac, lying south-east of the Landes and south of the middle Garonne. East and west, the upper Garonne and the Gave de Pau form bounding lines leading out from the plateau of Lannemezan, where the streams which spread fanlike in between take their rise. These have cut straight valleys through the alluvial detritus into the Tertiary *molasse*, leaving ridges with steep wooded scarps facing west and long fertile slopes to the east. The apex of the fan, around the town of Tarbes, is fully Pyrenean, but the lower table-lands (Armagnac) belong to Aquitaine. It is a country of wheat, maize and fruits, of geese and turkeys, and of expanding vineyards whose wines go to make Armagnac brandy. Auch, ancient cathedral city and capital of Gascony, is the chief market centre, midway between Tarbes and Agen.

4 The Garonne: Toulouse and Bordeaux

The low plateau of *molasse* in the angle between the Pyrenees and the Central Plateau is known as Lauraguais. The landscape is bare and windswept, the settlements concentrated in the sheltered valleys. A low watershed (the Col de Naurouze), separating intrenched streams which flow to the Garonne and to the Aude, gives access to the Gate of Carcassonne and to the Mediterranean. Road, railway and canal follow this route to Toulouse, where the Garonne turns as if designed by nature to carry on the line of movement direct to the Atlantic (see Fig. 20).

Toulouse, which is the largest city in the south-west of France, thus occupies an important site in relation to the Mediterranean entry. Here also come routes from the Pyrenees and from the north. The old part of the town lies on the high right bank of the river. Its nodal site, fixed by the Roman *Tolosa*, attracted influences from all sides in the Middle Ages, and the city became a great centre of intellectual and artistic life. A regional school of Romanesque architecture produced one of the most notable churches in France, the brick-built St. Sernin. Renaissance architecture is also well represented. In the 18th century and part of the 19th the Canal du Midi contributed to the prosperity of the town, but the railway robbed the wharves of their trade. The market of a wide agricultural area, Toulouse also acts as *entrepôt* between the Garonne basin and the Mediterranean, dealing especially in hides, cereals and wines. There are chemical, tobacco, leather and general metallurgical industries. The Toulouse region is noteworthy for the terraces that line the broad valley of the Garonne. Cereals, vines and vegetables are produced on their level surfaces, out of reach of floods.

The middle Garonne is the region where the Aveyron and the Lot join the river. Between Montauban (on the Tarn) and Marmande, its approximate limits, the towns are all on the north side of the rivers, where high banks gave protection from floods. Many of the smaller towns here and elsewhere in Aquitaine are of the *bastide* type, deliberately planted by French or English in the 12th, 13th and 14th centuries to encourage settlement after the ravages of the Albigensian wars. Their rectangular plans contrast sharply with the irregular plans of the older hill towns, though some settlements (e.g., Montauban) have a double origin related to hill and plain (cf. Carcassonne).

The middle Garonne is a fertile area of rich polyculture. To travel through its soft scenery is to understand the esteem in which these lands have been held by the English and by the dwellers among the wet hill-frames of Aquitaine. To the English this land of plenty seemed an earthly paradise. But because of the pull of Bordeaux and Toulouse it has not produced an outstanding centre of its own: Montauban, Moissac and Agen share its government and its commerce. Each district has its special crops and activities—notably Agen is the centre of plum-growing—but everywhere there is rich cultivation of the vine, wheat, maize, tobacco, asparagus, tomatoes, etc., both in the wide terraced valleys and on the limestone table-lands or *serres*.

Downstream the vine becomes more and more dominant as the department of Gironde is reached, embracing also the lower course of the Dordogne. A dozen miles above the confluence, on the left bank of the Garonne, is Bordeaux, the centre of the Bordelais wine district and also the outlet for the whole basin. Like Nantes, the town is placed where the river could be crossed without difficulty and where the tides bring enough water to carry ships up from the sea. The wine trade flourished in the days of English rule and has maintained itself ever since: indeed the concentration of the wine industry in the lower Garonne owes a good deal to the privileges formerly granted to Bordeaux. In addition it exports the resin and pit-props of the Landes, the latter going to South Wales in exchange for coal. Colonial links with tropical Africa and with the West Indies have led to imports of ground nuts, cocoa, sugar and bananas. Connections with South America are important.

Bordeaux, thanks to its remoteness, was chosen as a centre of important metallurgical industries in the war of 1914–18. The outport of Pauillac played an important part then, but it has not been able to compete with the more favourably-placed open-water ports of northern France in attracting the big liners and oil carriers. Pauillac deals chiefly in the timber of the Landes, and is the centre of the wine industry of Médoc, the pebble-floored peninsula between the Gironde and the sea. The alluvial promontory between the Garonne and the Dordogne (Entre-deux-Mers) is also under the vine, while Sauternes and Barsac are well-known centres farther up the Garonne.

Bordeaux and Toulouse were connected by pipe-line in 1957 to the natural-gas refineries at Lacq (see p. 156) under the Pyrenees. Considerable developments are likely to flow from this relatively cheap source of power, and if new industries can be attracted to Aquitaine, the result will be a better distribution of French economic activity, now so largely concentrated in the north and east. Already the aluminium industry has been attracted to Lacq, and plans are afoot to promote the industrialization of the Pau region. Another gas-field has been developed at Saint-Marcet, and the oil-field at Parentis in the Landes has been yielding since 1961.

Chapter 19

THE PYRENEES

1 *A Barrier Range*

From Toulouse or some other view-point in the Aquitaine lowlands the long snow-capped rampart of the Pyrenees closes the southern horizon. The continuity of this mountain barrier is most impressive. For 250 miles, from the Gulf of the Lion to the Bay of Biscay, the watershed maintains an almost straight line, and for nearly 200 miles it hardly drops below 5,000 feet. The peaks reach an average height of 10,000 feet, but they do not stand out boldly: the highest is the Pic d'Aneto (11,174 feet) in Spain.

The French and Spanish slopes are strongly contrasted. On the French side the mountains rise like a wall from the plains; the valleys are deep and short, having no marked longitudinal stretches. But on the south the Sierras of north Aragon form a broad sub-Pyrenean belt, between which and the main range the rivers draining to the Ebro have carved out longitudinal valleys.

The French Pyrenees are in consequence quite narrow, and owing to the difficulties of communication the valleys have tended to form communities connected with the plain rather than with each other. Historic interest attaches to the towns placed where the streams leave the mountains, and a *piedmont* zone of settlement and communication appears to be a feature of prehistoric antiquity.

But of greater interest to the story of France is the concentration of transverse ways of movement at both ends. In the western Pyrenees (west of the Somport pass) the hills are lower and only an occasional summit, e.g., Pic d'Anie, exceeds 6,500 feet. Several cols rise little above 3,000 feet and offer no serious difficulty to communications. This area corresponds approximately to the well-named department of Basses Pyrénées. The eastern Pyrenees, east of Andorra (where the department of Pyrénées Orientales begins) is also a region of passes. Towards the Mediterranean, moreover, the hills suddenly narrow, in the Mts. Albères, to an insignificant ridge, crossed by the Col du Perthus (under 1,000 feet) some 15 miles from the coast. At the west, the storied pass of Roncevaux (Roncesvalles), 3,500 feet high, is about 30 miles from the sea. The fame of these two terminal passes far overshadows that of all others, and to understand their significance in Pyrenean history we must consider briefly the physical relationships of their respective regions.

Broadly speaking, the range consists of a central core of crystalline and palaeozoic rocks, flanked by younger beds which are largely limestones. The older rocks form the high serrated backbone of the central Pyrenees. Towards the west, however, the core is much lower and the hills less massive, the structure lines are disturbed by the presence of an intrusive block known as the Basque massif. The proximity of the Atlantic has meant violent erosion, which is evident in the deep narrow valleys cut into plateau country, where the crest-lines lie at uniform heights.

Plateau surfaces are also characteristic of the eastern Pyrenees, where the ancient block of the Corbières limited the development of folds. These tend to run north-east and south-east, and the range is consequently broadest at this end. But as if to compensate for this, the mountain block has been fractured and sunken basins have resulted, giving an almost continuous belt of lowland along the Mediterranean shore. The foundering may be connected with the formation of the western Mediterranean deeps: it produced not only the broad depression of Roussillon, but also numerous foundered basins set amid the hills, e.g., those of Capcir and Cerdagne. Here, as in the western Pyrenees, the neighbouring sea has left its stamp on the character of the landscape. But it is a very different sea from that which breaks against the rocks at Biarritz and San Sebastian.

The climatic differences between the eastern and western ends of the Pyrenees are indeed striking: they so impressed the geographer Strabo that he thought the range must run from north to south. The Basque country is most fully exposed to the force of north-westerly gales, but oceanic conditions are carried well inland and the rainfall is heavy in the central as well as in the western Pyrenees. Sea-winds temper the heat of summer, and the winters are mild. In the east, the rainfall is low and confined to the winter half-year; the summers are very hot in the lowlands. It is, in fact, a fully Mediterranean climate.

These contrasts are reflected in the natural vegetation and in the human activities of Pyrenean lands. The Basque landscape, with its damp forests, cloudy skies and scattered farms, is reminiscent of many another Atlantic seaboard of Europe: the evergreen oaks and olive groves of the Corbières overlook the sun-baked plains and hill-towns of an entirely different physical and cultural environment.

Yet these terminal regions have certain characters in common, and they must be studied in relation to the Pyrenees as a whole. They have served as passage-ways by which the high central mountains could be turned. Through them have come many forces which have helped to mould the civilization of western Europe. Migrants and armies, crusaders, pilgrims, troubadours and craftsmen of all kinds have thronged the passes leading to Spain, while southern and even African influences have reached France, since Hannibal's day and long before, by the Mediterranean avenue between the hills and the sea.

It is true that these cultural movements died down when the Pyrenees became an established political frontier from end to end in the 17th century, but it is still by the eastern or western routes that the traveller passes from France to Spain, though neither the pass of Roncevaux nor the Col du Perthus has a railway. Moreover, a common way of life on both sides of the international frontier is reflected in the languages of the terminal regions. The Basque tongue is spoken by both French and Spanish citizens in the angle of the Bay of Biscay, and on the east the Catalan language of Catalonia is spoken in Roussillon.

2 *The Western Pyrenees*

Despite the fact that the Pyrenees are lower and narrower in the west, they are impressive enough as they are approached from the north, and near the coast bold peaks such as La Rhune are conspicuous. Underneath, foothills run out as far as the lower Adour, which forms the divide between the Basque country and the Landes. The river has, in fact, been driven south by encroaching dunes until it reached the hills. The picturesque Basque coast begins here. Its harbours, from Bayonne to Bilbao, were once the scene of great activity, notably from the 12th to the 17th century. Many adventurers, explorers and emigrants left this coast, and the Basque whalers were formerly famous. Nowadays the ports have become seaside resorts and tourist-traffic brings new activities to St. Jean-de-Luz and Hendaye. Biarritz is a luxurious modern town strikingly different from the old port, fortress and cathedral city of Bayonne, on the Adour. The frontier follows the river Bidassoa and the railway to Madrid crosses at Hendaye.

Inland, the Basque landscape and culture can be best observed in the valley of the Nive, which runs north-west to Bayonne. The Basques cling tenaciously to their language and customs, and their facial characteristics are at once recognizable. High-gabled farmsteads dot the still heavily-wooded landscape. Agriculture and stock-raising are combined with a good deal of smuggling across the frontier which divides the Basque country into two. St. Jean-Pied-de-Port is an old fortress-town at the foot of the pass of Roncevaux.

Farther east, the Gave d'Oloron comes down from the Pic du Midi d'Ossau. Oak and bracken give way to poplar-lined pastures in the valley floor, and fruits, maize and the vine are grown. In recent years the motor-coach has opened up this country, and hydro-electric power is being utilized. An electrified railway tunnels under the Somport pass to reach Jaca in the upper Aragon valley.

3 *The Central Pyrenees*

Beyond the Somport, the high Pyrenees continue as far as the upper Ariège. The streams fan out east and west to the

Garonne and the Adour, but they end in blind *culs-de-sac* under snow-clad peaks. The Cirque de Gavarnie is one of many high amphitheatres which the pleistocene glaciations carved out of the mountain sides. The frontier usually follows the crest-line, but the upper basin of the Garonne (the Val d'Aran) is in Spain. Such isolated mountain valleys long preserved their independence and in one of them (on the Spanish side of the divide) the Andorrans retain partial autonomy in their little republic, owing allegiance to both France and Spain. The common pastoral life of the high Pyrenees was formerly protected by treaties which allowed migrating flocks of sheep to cross the cols when the snows melted in summer. Transhumance is an important part of the economy of Andorra, and as in the Basque country smuggling is popular. The population numbers 11,000.

Large numbers of cattle and sheep are brought up to the high pastures in summer from the *piedmont* belt where the population has long been dense. The Gave de Pau is perhaps the most attractive of all the Pyrenean valleys. Tourist traffic and the rise of winter sports have brought fame and prosperity to its upper basin, but Lourdes and Pau are the historic centres. Lourdes is a fall-line market town, picturesquely placed where the Gave emerges from barren limestone hills to turn sharply left. It is an old route-centre, too, and this has helped it to become a pilgrimage place, the objects of attraction being the limestone grotto and miraculous spring. Lacq, near Pau, is the centre of a gas-field from which refined gas is piped to Toulouse and Bordeaux as well as to Pau and Bayonne.

Fields of wheat and maize, orchards and lush meadows accompany the Gave to Pau, with its celebrated view of the mountains, and to Orthez. North-east of Lourdes begins the broad expanse of ancient gravels known as Lannemezan. The Adour cuts through northwards before curving to the west. It has Bagnères de Bigorre and Tarbes on its banks, both market centres for the prosperous vales of Bigorrois. Tarbes, like Grenoble in the Alps, makes leather from lamb skins and is famous for horses—and Rugby football.

The Upper Garonne, crossing the frontier on leaving the

Val d'Aran, flows through a series of gorges and small basins to turn eastward at Montréjeau and so on through St. Gaudens to Toulouse. Near the point where it turns are St. Bertrand de Comminges, a small cathedral town of Roman origin, and the prehistoric Grotte de Gargas. Mineral wealth and medicinal waters have also provided inducement for settlement. Iron-working survives here and there, and several local industries such as paper making and woollen manufacture have been revived by hydro-electric power. The sub-Pyrenean railway has been electrified for some years.

The last section of the central Pyrenees lies in the department of Ariège, where the river of that name focuses the life of the area. The climate here is definitely drier, and some Mediterranean species—box, lavender and the evergreen oak —appear in the vegetation. But it is still a land of meadows and maize, and in common with the rest of the central Pyrenees it looks towards Toulouse and not to the Mediterranean. A trans-Pyrenean railway, connecting the upper Ariège with the upper Ter and Barcelona by the Col de Puymorens, has brought fresh life to the historic fortress-town of Foix.

4 The Eastern Pyrenees

In nearly every way this section of the range is a region apart. The drainage goes to the Mediterranean by the Aude, Têt and Tech, and Mediterranean vegetation is evident, in the thin *maquis* of the Corbières, in the cork oak woods of the Albères and in the pines and chestnuts of the higher mountains. The olive and the vine are widely grown, and the rich wines of Banyuls are celebrated. In the lowlands of Roussillon irrigation from mountain streams makes possible a varied cultivation of fruits, vegetables and fodder crops. Thus the plains are dependent upon the hills: the association between the two zones is nowhere more apparent than in Roussillon. The great pyramid of Canigou, snow-capped in winter, dominates the plain and is held in legendary veneration by the peoples of the Têt and Tech valleys. On the former river is Perpignan, capital of Roussillon, once a fortress guarding the road to Spain.

Going upstream we pass by Prades and Mont Louis over the

Col de la Perche into the high level plains of Cerdagne in the upper Sègre valley. Though on the south side of the watershed, part of this belongs to France. The villagers of Cerdagne, in fact, utilize the pastures of the Carlitte, and this economic dependence was recognized by the Treaty of the Pyrenees in 1659.

The Aude takes its rise in the basin of Capcir, cut off by deep gorges from the lower valley to the north, where Carcassonne is related to its corridor and to Languedoc rather than to the local life of the Pyrenees.

Despite the differences that exist between the three main sections of the mountains described above, the Pyrenees have strong regional unity of life and function. They form the most definite land frontier of France; and the capital importance of the two ends for the study of the growth of French consciousness is to be related to the negative function of the central Pyrenees as a barrier. Moreover, in all sections, the mountains have given rise to local centres that form a string of urban settlements and a line of movement from sea to sea. And under the snows of the high summits as well as among the misty hills of the Basque country old communities have kept a show of the independence bred of the mobility and freedom of life in isolated pastoral uplands.

Chapter 20

THE MEDITERRANEAN COASTLANDS
AND THE LOWER RHÔNE

1   *A Barrier River*

Structurally, the Rhône valley below Lyon cannot be considered apart from the Saône valley, and historically they have together formed a great highway between north and south. But the regional affinities of the corridor south of 46° N.—approximately the latitude of Lyon—are with the Midi rather than with Burgundy. Hereabouts the trough narrows considerably as the Jura gives way to the foreland of Dauphiny where the Rhône breaks through from the Swiss plateau. The valley widens again below Valence, the Cévennes swinging away to the south-west and the Alps falling back somewhat towards Marseille, to leave between them a broad triangle of lowlands with its base on the coast.

The coastlands west of the Rhône, including the lower Aude basin under the Pyrenees, make up Languedoc. East of the river lies Provence, embracing lowlands along the river, valleys among the southern Alps, and the indented Riviera coast. There is thus much diversity in the component parts of this region, and though the Rhône is the smallest of the three principal river-basins of France, it has been characterized by disunity. The broad swift-flowing river has always imposed a barrier between east and west, and it presents many difficulties to navigation.

Irregular in flow, the Rhône is further liable to the formation of gravel banks which seriously impede traffic. Upstream navigation was slight even in former days when the rivers were more important as lines of communication. The great Alpine feeders, Isère and Durance, add to the complexity by contributing great quantities of mud and gravel and of flood water

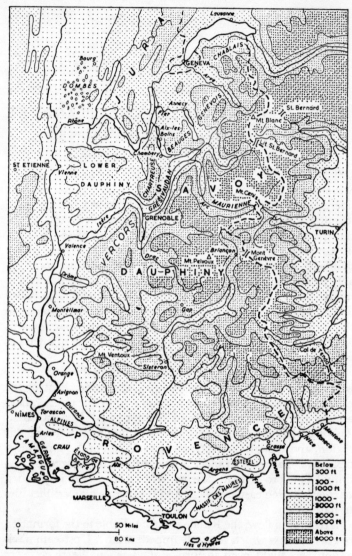

Figure 21 The French Alps and Provence
(For Languedoc see Fig. 19, p. 134)

from melted snows. On the right bank, too, the Cévennes streams, Ardèche and Gard, cause sudden rises and falls in the main stream.

Below Orange the river flows above the level of its flood-plain and it frequently divides around long marshy islands. It cuts through a low ridge of limestone at Avignon and finally breaks into its two main deltaic arms at Arles, nearly 30 miles from the sea. The largest branch, the Grand Rhône, goes to the east, and has extended its section of the delta much farther out than that of the Petit Rhône.

Westwards the alluvial plain, composed of silt carried with the currents, runs in a narrow strip towards Cette. Long sand-spits line the curving coast of Languedoc and Roussillon, leaving lagoons strung out behind them. Here and there, as at Cette and Agde, lumps of limestone or lava break the monotony of the coastal flats. Inland, too, low ridges of limestone, stray offshoots of the Pyrenean folds diverted by the Corbières massif, diversify the landscape of Languedoc, while volcanic hills related to the eruptions of the Central Plateau stand out under the Cévennes.

East of the lower Rhône, the axis of the lowlands runs north and south, not east and west. Sharp ridges of limestone, such as the Chaîne des Alpines, cross the plains, but the rise to the Alps is well defined north of the Durance, where Mont Ventoux rears up its white head. The Durance crosses the plain near Avignon, but its upper basin belongs definitely to the Alpine region. We are concerned in this chapter only with the southernmost folds, which rarely touch 3,000 feet and are broken by sunken valleys where conditions are Mediterranean. Still more broken is the country east of Toulon, for here, under the ancient block of the Maures, a continuous depression drained by the river Argens opens up an east-west route through Provence.

The coast, from Toulon to the Italian frontier at Mentone, consists of a succession of promontories separated by sheltered creeks and bays, and fringed by rocky islets. Favoured by nature, this Riviera coast has become famous for its rich cultivation and its winter resorts. The whole Provençal coast abounds in harbours, some of which have been utilized throughout historic time.

Provence and Languedoc have the climate, vegetation and modes of life associated with the Mediterranean. The Rhône corridor between Lyon and Montélimar shows features transitional between the Midi and the north. North of Valence a marked if short period of dry weather in summer is already apparent, but the January temperature is below 40° and it falls rapidly towards the Saône basin. The long summer drought becomes definitely established south of Valence; the olive makes its appearance, and stretches of thorny scented *maquis* alternate with dazzling limestone exposures. The mulberry, however, can withstand more winter cold and it is grown as far north as Lyon, while the evergreen oak is found almost as far north. Coastal Provence under the hills is even milder in winter and hotter in summer, and here the orange and lemon are added to the olive where there is shelter from the northerly wind. This wind, known as the Mistral, is very strong and cold in the open plains of the lower Rhône, where screens of reeds and belts of cypress are used to break its force (Pl. VIII).

We described in Chapter 5 some of the ways in which man has modified the natural environment of Mediterranean France. It now remains for us to consider the functions of the region as a whole before dealing with its present-day activities. Its functional unity resides in its relations with the civilization of the Mediterranean and with the two gateways leading past Lyon and Carcassonne to the other lowlands of France. We remember that the first Roman "province" was established here, that Greek colonies lined the coast centuries earlier, and that in mediaeval days crusaders and merchants brought many contacts with the Levant. Roman civilization took firm root in the Midi and left behind cities which are rich in memorials of the past. Urban life is as characteristic of the south as the clear sky or the blue sea; and it flourishes notably on the coast of Provence, where Marseille and Toulon have between them a population of nearly a million.

Languedoc, however, has suffered since Roman times by the silting up of its old harbours, e.g., Narbonne. The

Roman heritage is stronger and deeper in Provence than in Languedoc, and differences of outlook can be detected in the modern populations. It has been said that while Languedoc is critical Provence is sceptical, "Christian by conversion but pagan by heritage". The contrasts between Arles and Nîmes cannot fail to strike the visitor.

In the Renaissance, the Rhône corridor became once more a pathway for the revived classical learning, and if later on the attention of Europe was drawn rather towards the New World, the opening of the Suez Canal and the development of French possessions in Africa and in the Far East brought new life to Marseille and its hinterland. The Rhône valley today, with its left and right bank railways, its great barrages and canals (see p. 168), is busier than it has ever been since the early traders found a way through the forests to the north.

2 *The Rhône Corridor*

Lyon owes its enduring fame to the convergence of routes at the junction of Rhône and Saône, routes from the Loire, from Switzerland and Italy as well as from north and south. It is the gateway of the Midi, and a place of considerable influence in political and literary affairs. The modern expansion of the city, which has extended rapidly over the morainic country to the east of the rivers, is largely based on the silk industry, founded originally by Italian immigrants. About 80 per cent of France's silk production comes from Lyon, and it may be recalled that silk is the most valuable export of France. Some of the raw material is obtained from the Rhône basin, but the bulk is imported from Italy and from the east. To the neighbouring hill regions the town owes its supplies of industrial power (coal and hydro-electricity) and also of skilled human material, for men as well as waters go downhill from the mountains. As a great textile town it is important in the chemical industry. A new town, Villeurbanne, has recently been established in its eastern suburbs.

St. Etienne with its coal-field, lying on a route through the rim of the Central Plateau between Lyon and the Loire, belongs economically to the Rhône basin. In addition to specialized textile production (ribbons) under the influence of Lyon, the town is a centre of metallurgical industries.

On the Rhône, Vienne occupies the first of a series of small basins which together compose the corridor between Lyon and Valence. An important centre in Roman times, its once famous woollen industry has given way to silk production, carried on in many parts of this area. The next town of the string that lines the river on the left bank is Valence, in a nest of alluvial terraces built up by Rhône and Isère. The landscape has orchards and vineyards as well as wheat and rows of mulberry, and maize becomes less common.

3 *Provence*

Below Valence the valley narrows to about a mile, widening again at Montélimar and entering soon after a countryside that is unmistakably Mediterranean. We are now in Provence proper, as the olive groves tell us; wine, wheat and olives constitute the material basis of life. The almond appears also. From here to the delta the railway passes through Orange, Avignon, Tarascon and Arles, old towns in which the rich life of the Rhône plain is concentrated. Orange commanded the road north, while the other three controlled crossings of the Rhône. The broken bridge of St. Bénézet at Avignon bears witness to the fury of the river, above which rises the 14th-century Palace of the Popes. Opposite is the border fortress of Villeneuve, built by the French kings when Avignon was in this area. Les Baux, 15 miles to the south, gives its name to bauxite and reminds us that France is the leading producer of aluminium in Europe. The railway crosses the Rhône by a huge suspension bridge from Tarascon to Beaucaire in Languedoc.

The Roman crossing was at the head of the delta, at Arles, which became the chief port of the river. Arles preserves several fine monuments of both Roman and Romanesque architecture (Pl. II). The delta is known as the Camargue—for centuries a solitude of wind-swept marshlands. A few shepherds and herdsmen lived in the drier parts, where the chief occupation was the rearing of fighting bulls. For the rest, apart from some

solitude of wind-swept marshlands. A few shepherds and herdsmen lived in the drier parts, where the chief occupation was
the rearing of fighting bulls. For the rest, apart from some
activity in shooting and fishing and the winning of salt by
evaporation, little use could be made of this wasteland except
as a sanctuary for wildfowl. Since 1942 great changes have
affected nearly a third of its 200,000 acres. Irrigation water
pumped from the Rhône and distributed by hundreds of miles
of channels supports over 2,000 rice farms which are able to
supply the bulk of the French consumption, replacing former
imports from Indo-China.

Another distinctive *pays* is Crau, which lies east of the delta
and south of the Alpines chain. Consisting of stony detritus
brought down by the Durance when it flowed (in a former
course) in this direction, Crau long remained a waste. Though
large areas are still unproductive or given over to sheep, in
other parts irrigation has enabled a wide range of crops to be
grown. The sheep have to be removed in the summer, when
they are taken—nowadays by rail for the most part—to the
pastures of the high Alps. This transhumance, an ancient
feature of life in summer-drought regions, is less important
than formerly: reafforestation of the Alps, for one thing, has
limited its extent.

Aix, the old capital of Provence, is at the edge of the hills
where the depression that runs eastward to the Argens valley
begins. It owes its metropolitan character partly to a position
where it could keep in touch with the diverse parts of the
region. Aix is the centre of the olive-oil trade, but its prosperity
has been affected by the economic attraction of Marseille.

This great seaport, the busiest of all Mediterranean ports,
has its nucleus around a small rock basin protected from the
force of the Mistral—the site of the original Greek *Massalia*.
Deep water along shore and freedom from silting give it advantages in modern times, so that it has become the outlet of
the Rhône basin; and with a population of 778,000 it is the
second city of France, though it has had to contend with steep
hill-slopes and difficult terrain between the port and the
Provençal plain. We have drawn attention in Chapter 10 to

the development of the Étang de Berre as an inland harbour and industrial extension of Marseille.

The port of Marseille became the chief collecting and distributing centre for the French colonies. It is a great port of call and of passenger traffic. Its imports are largely raw materials —oil-seeds, silk and tropical products—and its exports manufactured goods. Industries, grouped along the coast, include chemical works, sugar refineries, and the manufacture of soap, candles and margarine. The town is closely linked with the other Mediterranean seaports and its cosmopolitan population includes many Italians and Algerians.

East of Marseille the hills close in and are mostly wooded or devoted to sheep-rearing. The contorted coast is rich in harbours, and one of the largest shelters the naval port of Toulon. The islands of Hyères are remnants of the ancient land mass also preserved in the Maures and in Corsica and Sardinia. Impermeable rocks produce a changed landscape, and the inhabitants of the Maures live in hamlets scattered through wooded valleys where the chestnut has been an important article of diet. Routes through the depression to the north, coming from Aix and Avignon, reach the coast at Fréjus, once a Roman port.

Here the Riviera proper begins, a limestone country facing south-east and sheltered from the north winds. Cannes, Antibes, Nice, Monaco and Mentone are the leading resorts, old Provençal towns which have prospered with the rise of tourist traffic. Flowers, citrus fruits and vegetables are produced both for local and distant markets, and Grasse, inland from Cannes, is the centre of the perfumery industry. The population of Nice approaches 300,000.

4 Languedoc[1]

Compared with Provence, Languedoc is less rich in nearly every way. The high ridge of the Cévennes blocks communication northward, while the silted coast attracts little shipping and comparatively few tourists. Though it has easy access to Aquitaine and to Roussillon and Spain by Narbonne, these

[1] See Fig. 19, p. 134.

routes cannot compare with the great thoroughfare of the Rhône, however much they meant in the past. Its agriculture is poorer, too, and it has not the wealth of urban life characteristic of Provence. Nîmes and Montpellier, its largest towns, both have about 100,000 inhabitants: there is no centre at all comparable with Marseille or with Lyon.

Nîmes is on the edge of the folded hill country which occupies roughly half of the area between the Cévennes and the sea. The low hills ("Garrigues") are thinly clothed with broom and prickly plants, but the valleys are fertile and the vine is grown extensively. Now one of the chief centres of the wine trade, Nîmes was a wealthy Roman town, and it revived as a centre of industry in Protestant hands. Many small industries are today dependent on coal derived largely from the Alais field nearby. South of Nîmes, the building out of the Rhône delta has affected such ports as the mediaeval Aigues Mortes ("stagnant waters"), an almost fossilized Crusader town.

Montpellier is the headquarters of the wine industry of Hérault, which produces more wine than any other department of France. The town is celebrated for its University and especially for the Faculty of Medicine which profited from contacts with Arab learning during the Middle Ages. From here to the sea runs a ridge of limestone off the end of which currents have formed spits enclosing the Étang de Thau. Cette is built partly on the ridge and partly on the sand-spit. The once flourishing life of this littoral survives in the fisheries of Cette and in a small coastal traffic in agricultural products. Canals link it up with Bordeaux and with the Rhône. Irrigation is diversifying crops and increasing yields in this area. Agde (Greek *Agatha*) lies under basalt hills which give the coast a changed direction near the mouth of the river Hérault. The fortress town of Béziers is now a wine-centre of fair size.[1]

With the Aude valley and Narbonne and Carcassonne we

[1] Ambitious plans to irrigate the coastal land between the Rhône delta and Béziers by means of canals leading from the Rhône are coming to fruition. The aim is to supplement the declining wine-production of Languedoc by growing vegetables and orchard-crops. The project is in charge of the *Compagnie Nationale d'Aménagement de la Region du Bas-Rhône et du Languedoc.*

reach the western limits of Languedoc. A seaport until the 14th century, Narbonne also marked the junction of the ways from Spain and from Aquitaine, and above all the place where the Garonne route from Bordeaux reached the Mediterranean. The plains west of Narbonne are under the vine, but the landscape takes on a different character as the valley of the Aude closes in and the Montagne Noire is approached. Structure, climate and vegetation change more abruptly than in the Rhône valley: the olive disappears; and at Carcassonne, 40 miles from the sea, we reach the famous fortress city which guarded through successive ages the approach from Toulouse by way of the gap between the Central Plateau and the Pyrenees.

Note.—THE RHÔNE VALLEY AUTHORITY

The Compagnie Nationale du Rhône was authorized as long ago as 1921, in the period of rehabilitation following the First World War, but apart from the building of the great dam at Génissiat near the Swiss frontier it was not until after the Second World War that what has been called "the modernization of one of mankind's oldest thoroughfares" was seriously tackled. In 1954 the Donzère-Mondragon barrage, north of Avignon, came into operation as the first of several schemes designed to harness the power of the Rhône, to improve navigation and to provide water for irrigation. The dam, which ponds back the river for six miles, is by-passed by a canal 160 yards wide. The construction has been described as the greatest engineering achievement of its kind in western Europe, demonstrating the genius of the French in this field. Near Avignon, too, at Marcoule, plutonium and electricity for industrial use are produced in atomic piles. Another great dam has been completed at Pierre-Bénite near Lyon. Plans to extend the Rhône navigation have been discussed for some time: they include the construction of a canal from the river through Switzerland, and the improvement of the present Rhône–Rhine and Saône–Moselle canals.

Chapter 21

THE FRENCH ALPS

1 *An Un-born Switzerland*

We are so accustomed to think of the Alps of Switzerland, Austria and Italy, that we are apt to forget how large a part of the Alpine system is included in France. Some three-quarters of the western section of the mountains, south of Lake Geneva, belong to France; the Italian frontier following the watershed, which lies well to the eastern side. This reverses the position of the divide in the Pyrenees, where it leaves only a narrow strip on the French side.

The length of this Alpine territory, from north to south, if we include the mountains of Provence, is about equal to that of the Pyrenees, but its breadth is on the average three times as great. Though it rises to nearly 16,000 feet in Mont Blanc, however, and is in other parts higher than the highest Pyrenean crests, it is not so effective a barrier as the Pyrenees. Great valleys opening into the heart of the mountains lead to passes which have been utilized from the earliest times. These and other differences in nature and human life are based on structural facts (see Fig. 21).

The western Alps are built up of parallel zones extending roughly north and south from Lake Geneva and the middle Rhône towards Provence. The easternmost zone is the High Alps, formed of rocks that are mainly crystalline and including Mont Blanc and Mont Pelvoux. To the west of this is a narrow longitudinal trench worn out of Liassic shales and occupied by a series of river basins of which the upper Isère is the chief. It is followed through most of its length by lines of communication and in it are the largest towns of the French Alps—Grenoble and Chambéry.

Outside this depression is a belt of limestone uplands known as the pre-Alps, consisting of ranges folded like the Jura, but more violently, rising to about half the height of the crystalline zone. The pre-Alps are crossed by four steep-walled transverse valleys through which waters drain to the Rhône; and these gates play a controlling part in the economy of the Alps. They are occupied by the Arve, going down to Geneva, by Lakes Annecy and Bourget, and by the Isère. This belt is thus divided into five blocks, each with its own name (Chablais, Genevois, Bauges, Chartreuse and Vercors) and a degree of individuality. South of Vercors—the southernmost of these blocks—the pre-Alps widen out towards the lower Durance region, where the ranges swing eastwards in conformity with the trend of the Provençal system.

To the north-west of the pre-Alps, between the middle Rhône and the lower Isère, a fourth belt of country, largely composed of detritus, forms the Alpine foreland of Lower Dauphiny, which reaches its farthest extent about Lyon. Above the cold morainic deposits the edge of the pre-Alps rises abruptly and, catching the clouds, is rich in meadowland and forest.

The high crystalline Alps are snow-clad throughout the year above an average height of 9,000 feet, and the highest parts are scored with glaciers. Glacial phenomena can be well studied in the Mont Blanc massif (e.g., Mer de Glace), but the whole Alpine region was invaded by ice in the Pleistocene period, and bears the imprint of tremendous erosion. The valleys are deeply cut and the tributary streams are left "hanging" above them. At various levels on the valley sides are ledges and hollows (cirques) that sometimes meet on opposite slopes and produce narrow jagged ridges. Not only is the relief profoundly modified by such ice erosion, but the stage for human action was in many particulars set by it (Pl. III).

Stock-raising is everywhere the main occupation of the High Alps, but it is combined with cultivation in a complicated economy operating with the seasons and utilizing the vertical variations of vegetation and climate. Isolation has preserved these ancient communities down to the present day, though for the last century or so emigration has been a serious factor. New influences which must affect the local life but which will check depopulation are the growth of the tourist industry and the exploitation of hydro-electric power. To some extent, too, the main valleys have been drawn into the trans-Alpine traffic that crosses by the Mt. Cénis tunnel to Turin.

Through this Alpine territory the watershed, as a rule, marks the frontier between France and Italy, and under modern conditions this arrangement works fairly well. But it was not until 1860 that the crest-line became the international divide in the northern part of the area. Here the Dukes of Savoy had for centuries controlled the passes through the Alps—the Little St. Bernard, the Fréjus and the Mt. Cénis. Not until the passes had finally fallen into disuse did French rule extend to the watershed. The independence of the mountain folk showed itself in the strong resistance put up by heretical sects to persecution in the Middle Ages. But the French Alps as a whole never developed a unity to compare with the political organization of the Swiss cantons. In Switzerland the wide lake-plateau between the Alps and the Jura provided centres of communication and administration, but farther south the corresponding depression between High Alps and pre-Alps is too confined and not sufficiently central to act as a regional focus on the same scale. The region has been described as "an unborn Switzerland".

2 *Dauphiny and Savoy*

We may conveniently begin our description with the Alpine foreland of Lower Dauphiny. The higher stretches of this moraine-strewn tract are forested. The dry stony terraces have been improved and cultivated, while the damp hollows have been turned into meadows. Industrial development came with the exploitation of power from the streams, and in modern times the area has been drawn into the economic orbit of Lyon. Even the smallest villages, supplied with electric power, carry on silk-weaving, but there are no towns of any size.

Behind Lower Dauphiny the main gate through the pre-Alps opens along the Isère to Grenoble, which, lying in the longitudinal trench, commands routes coming from many directions and occupies a site utilized from Roman days. Market town and fortress in the Middle Ages, Grenoble is now

famous as the chief centre of glove-making in France, an industry related to the Alpine supply of lambskins. Grenoble played
a pioneering part in the transmission and utilization of hydro-
electric power, now widely used for industrial purposes in and
around the Alps. The Isère trough above the town, known as
Grésivaudan, has developed paper, chemical and engineering
works in villages long devoted to the routine of agricultural
life and transhumance. Here, at Tignes, is a spectacular 600-
foot-high dam for hydro-electric power.

Grenoble (pop. 157,000) is something of an Alpine metropo-
lis: it has excellent communications and a considerable volume
of tourist traffic, though Chambéry is a more important railway centre. This town, the old capital of Savoy, lies where the
Lake Bourget depression meets the Grésivaudan, on the main
route through the Alps to Mt. Cénis. It occupies a fertile vale
in which vine and fruit culture are carried on. Nearby, on the
lake, the springs of Aix-les-Bains have given rise to a fashionable health-resort. Towards Mont Blanc, the third transverse
break in the pre-Alps carries the Lake of Annecy: the town at
its lower end is the market for a rich cultivated area extending
to the Jura. It gets power from the Fier which carries the over-
flow of the lake through a great gorge to reach the Rhône.

Still farther on, the Arve takes the drainage of Mont Blanc
towards Geneva, forming a deep trench of which the upper
section is the Vale of Chamonix. Numerous small industries,
old and new, are operated with electricity and the volume of
tourist traffic recalls many a Swiss valley.

The pre-Alps, as we have noticed, fall into five blocks separated by gaps. These blocks are all well-watered and rich in
forests and pastures. Seasonal migration of cattle is the rule,
and pastoral life is most highly developed in the northernmost
sub-division—Chablais. The massif between Lake Bourget and
the Isère—known as Grande Chartreuse—takes its name from
the famous religious establishment of that name. This area is
still densely forested and the population is scanty. Vercors is a
more regular folded mass south of the Isère: it broadens out
into the thinly-peopled upland drained by the Drôme, flowing west to the Rhône. Here, to the Alps of Dauphiny, come

many of the sheep which leave Provence in summer. To the east, the longitudinal corridor continues south from Grenoble and is occupied by the river Drac, coming down from Mont Pelvoux. Industry has taken hold in a number of small towns along this valley.

On the other side of Mt. Pelvoux we come to the valley of the upper Durance, which follows a course roughly from north to south and concentrates the drainage of the southern part of our region. Briançon, near its source, is at a meeting of ways over the cols from the Isère valley and from Italy, the Col de Mt. Genèvre being the most famous of these. The little town lies in a sheltered basin where southern fruits—almonds and apricots as well as plums—are grown and where sheep spend the winters. Gap and Sisteron lower down the river are old route-centres on the roads from Provence and Dauphiny into Italy. Mediterranean influences are felt about Sisteron, and the mountains decline in height as we pass down the Durance into Provence.

3 *Mountain Economy*

The ancient background of seasonal mountain life in the French Alps can still be studied in the high valleys of Savoy, perhaps best of all where the Arc opens a way towards Mt. Cénis from the Isère. This region is known as Maurienne, and may be taken as typical of the high valley-regions. Soils for cultivation and for meadows, and fairly level sites for building are provided by the ledges which break the steep mountain sides: often these ledges lie in series, one above the other, each having a group of habitations. A larger village usually occupies the lowest ledge, or nestles against an alluvial fan above the valley floor. This is the permanent settlement, for the other châlets are as a rule used only in spring and summer. In spring the flocks and herds are driven up to the meadows freed from winter snow, and most of the village goes up with them. As the snow melts from the highest ledges and from the mountain slopes above the forests, men and animals continue their march uphill, to return as winter approaches. Meanwhile some of the villagers have descended to the valley to harvest the crops of hay and cereals and to pick the fruits, among which the vine normally figures.

In winter, the cattle are kept in the valley, and butter and cheese are made. The organization of co-operative societies (fruitières) has spread here from the Jura and Switzerland. The summer flocks of sheep are augmented in many areas by those which come up by rail from Provence.

The old mountain economy, ingeniously related to specialized environmental conditions, could only survive in an isolation that is now breaking down. Life in the richer valleys and in the larger cities—Lyon and Paris—has attracted the Savoyard for many decades. It remains to be seen whether the invasion of power-plants and sightseers will keep the mountain folk at home. However that may be, the prosperity of the larger valleys of the pre-Alps, and of Grenoble, Chambéry and Annecy, promises to be a permanent feature of the life of the region.

Communications were further improved with the completion, in 1965, of a seven-mile road-tunnel to Italy, passing through Mont Blanc at a height of 4,000 feet.

Chapter 22

CORSICA AND THE FRENCH COMMUNITY

1 *Corsica*

The island of Corsica, which is one of the Metropolitan departments of France, compares with its neighbour Sardinia in being a remnant of an ancient land-mass which once occupied much of what is now the western Mediterranean sea. It is composed of granite and schist and forms a dissected plateau with steep faces, rising abruptly from deep marine basins to heights which approach 9,000 feet in Mt. Cinto. The only lowland of any extent, the plain of Aleria, lies on the east coast; the western side of the island is deeply eroded by streams running southwest along Hercynian lines and reaching the sea in a succession of drowned gulfs that break the contour of the coast on this side.

Corsica has a Mediterranean climate, considerably modified by elevation and free from intense drought for the same reason. Dense *maquis* occupies wide areas, but the intermediate mountain slopes, especially in the east and north-west, are clothed with magnificent forests of chestnut and Corsican pine. The chestnut is a staple article of diet, and where it is found are found also the isolated pastoral communities most characteristic of Corsica. Sheep, cheese and leather are the typical products. This native life is best developed in the richer upland basins draining to the east coast. Corte and Venaco are the chief centres.

The coastlands have the olive and almond, citrus fruits and wheat, but they have been retarded historically by the dangers of maritime marauders and by malaria. The coastal towns, e.g., Bastia and Bonifacio, usually had their origins in fortresses, and they have had few relations with the interior. The railway from Ajaccio to Bastia has to climb to nearly 4,000 feet to cross the island. Ajaccio (24,000) is the capital; its history reflects the troubled life of coasts which most of the sea powers and pirates of the Mediterranean have touched in turn. Thus retarded, and impoverished by a difficult environment, the mountain people of Corsica have lagged behind the general life of the Mediterranean. There is a good deal of emigration to France and other areas overseas. Tourist traffic is increasing and is a considerable source of revenue; there are air connections with the European mainland and ship routes to France and Italy.

2 *The French Community: historical*

Since 1954 France has been involved in the painful process of decolonization. In that year her overseas possessions had an area of 4½ million square miles and a population of 65 millions. In 1958, when President de Gaulle took office, the Constitution of the Fifth Republic establishing the French Community was approved by referendum. The colonial empire was dissolved, all areas voting for the Constitution except French Guinea, which left the community but which has, none-theless, co-operated with France in economic and cultural matters since 1963. Other states which declared their complete independence in 1960 (mostly in West Africa) have since entered into similar agreements with France. Algeria's independence was overwhelmingly approved by a referendum in Metropolitan France in 1962, but France extends to her former colony substantial aid and her petroleum resources are being developed under a joint organization. The bulk of the former colonial territories in tropical Africa, however, are member states of the French Community. Other categories of membership are Overseas Departments, which send several deputies to the National Assembly, and Overseas Territories, which send one or more deputies.

The story of French colonial expansion falls into two main chapters. In common with other West European countries, France established many overseas connections during the period of maritime expansion in the 16th and 17th centuries. This chapter opens with the voyages of Bretons and Normans— the French equivalent of the Men of Devon—to Newfoundland

and the St. Lawrence valley. A relic of this early enterprise is the group of small islands off the south coast of Newfoundland known as St. Pierre and Miquelon, which are cod-fishing centres. They rank as an Overseas Territory. The French later gained a foothold in the West Indies, and also in West Africa, which was then closely linked economically with the West Indies through the Atlantic "triangular" trade and the demand for slaves on the plantations. Following the sea-routes to the East, Réunion and Mauritius, in the Indian Ocean, were taken in the 17th and early 18th century. The former became an Overseas Department of the French Republic in 1946, while Mauritius retains the French language although its ownership passed to Britain in 1814. The small colonies that France established in the first phase of expansion have a value that is mainly historical and sentimental, but they have given her a number of able scholars, artists and administrators. The Overseas Departments include, besides Réunion, French Guiana and the islands of Martinique and Guadeloupe in the Lesser Antilles. In India French influence reached its greatest extension in the middle of the 18th century, but the clash with the stronger power of Britain brought defeat; and loss of nearly all her possessions in the East and in North America followed soon afterwards. The last Indian relics of the French Empire—Pondicherry and three smaller trading ports—were ceded to India in 1954.

The second chapter opens in the 19th century, when France took a prominent part in the opening up and partitioning of North Africa from 1830 onwards; and her colonial interests and ambitions became closely associated with that continent. Northwest Africa—known to history as Barbary—belongs to the Mediterranean region in its physique and climate, and in the Roman period it was part of the Mediterranean cultural world. It was in Algeria that France made her most massive experiment in colonization. Some coastal areas of West Africa, e.g., Senegal, had been French territory since the 17th century but it was not until the second half of the 19th century and the early 20th that, with increasing rivalries among the colonial pioneers, France laid claim to the hinterlands and consolidated her African conquests. In the world war of 1914–18 her African possessions were increased by the addition of the greater part of the former German colonies of the Cameroons and Togoland, other parts of which passed under British control. With the upsurge of African nationalism after the second world war some parts of the severed territories were united as the independent republics of Togo (1960) and Cameroon (1961).

In the Far East, France had an early missionary interest in Annam, but it was not until 1858 that a military expedition began an infiltration that led to the foundation of French Indo-China in 1899. After Japanese occupation from 1940 to 1945 the French re-established themselves in Cochin-China—the Delta of the Mekong River—but the following year hostilities broke out, which turned into civil war after the French withdrew in 1954. Cambodia became independent in 1955, Laos has had more troubled independence, while Vietnam became the cockpit of a new power-clash in which China and the U.S.A. are involved.

Finally the Pacific Ocean was also involved in French colonization, and the Community includes a number of island groups: French Polynesia (mainly the Society Archipelago with Tahiti) and New Caledonia. These two groups rank as overseas territories, as do the few scattered French possessions in Antarctica.

In its dispersion, the colonial empire of France, strung along the seaways of the world, once rivalled that of Britain. The language and culture of France survive, however, not only in French Africa but in several areas which have long ceased to be French politically, notably in Quebec and to a lesser extent in New Orleans. In Quebec an active minority of the French-speaking population is agitating for political independence. French is preserved also among settlers in the Argentine and Uruguay.

3 *French Africa*

It is necessary to look more closely at French Africa, which was France's major achievement as a colonizing power and to which she is bound by many historical, cultural and economic ties. With the exception of French Somaliland, at the entrance to the Red Sea—which ranks as an Overseas Territory—and the Malagasy Republic (Madagascar)—which is a member state of the Community—the former African colonies of France form a compact block extending from the Barbary coast to beyond the equator, near the mouth of the River Congo. This is a distance of 3,000 miles, and the distance from west to east, from Cape Verde to the Sudan, is little less. It is true that the now independent states of this vast area stand in varying relationships with the French Community. At the moment of writing (1965) some of the former colonies are full member states of the Community (Central African Republic, Republic of Congo, Republic of Gabon, the Republic of Senegal and the Republic of Chad); others have agreed to co-operate in various ways with the Community (the Ivory Coast, Mali, Guinea, Dahomey, Upper Volta, Mauritania, Niger and the Republics of Togo and Cameroon); while there are separate agreements between France and Algeria. What may be called the French area, or the Franc Zone,[1] extends from the North Sea to the Congo, balanced on either side of the meridian which runs through Paris, Algiers and Dahomey. The Western Mediterranean—almost a French lake—is a short break which unites rather than separates the coasts of France and Algeria. The maintenance of economic, strategic and cultural links with this great block of territory running deep into the tropics is a challenge to French diplomacy. A generous spirit of universalism runs through French civilization, and few Frenchmen would admit that there is any higher culture in the western world. The New France is very conscious of her standing in the civilized world, and in the words of an official spokesman, "More than any other nation, she feels impelled to spread the influence of her civilization." France ranks next to the United States of America in the provision of aid to the developing countries of the world, and in relation to its gross national product it comes easily first. Much of this aid goes to French

[1] In fact the Franc Zone also includes (in Africa) Morocco, Tunisia, Madagascar and Somaliland, as well as the Overseas Departments and Overseas Territories.

Africa, and in giving it she risks being accused of neo-colonialism.

It has been said that the French have not made good colonists but have tried to remain good Frenchmen wherever they have settled. The very perfection of their cultural adaptation to the French environment, it seems, rendered them ill-fitted to settlement outside the homeland, and especially to pioneering, in which the Scots and Irish, for example, have excelled. "The Frenchman will not settle out of hearing and sight of others." It was France's aim to turn the Africans into French citizens, and she had the tolerant Latin attitude towards racial differences, so that intermarriage carried no stigma. Thus the colonial policies of France differed markedly from those of Great Britain, which, officially at least, maintained the colour-bar and did not mix with "the natives". The French system naturally worked best in areas which were geographically similar to the homeland, and this helps to explain the development of Algeria as "more than a colony", as an overseas homeland, which was divided like France into departments and directly represented in the French Assembly. (It is interesting to reflect that British colonialism, on the other hand, was least successful in an area such as Ireland, adjacent to her shores.) Nearly 2 million settlers of French descent were established in Algeria, among a native Moslem population of about 9 millions. But the forces of African nationalism proved too strong for the colonists. In 1954 the National Liberation Front in Algeria went over to open warfare, and terrorism spread alarmingly in Metropolitan France. In the following years nearly ¾ million settlers returned to France. Finally in 1962 a settlement was reached and Algeria became an independent republic, with Arabic as its official language and French as the principal foreign language.

The Algerian coastlands (the Tell) between the northern ranges of the Atlas Mountains and the Mediterranean Sea, settled by the French, are economically the most advanced parts of Algeria and of French Africa. Along the 700 miles of coast, with its crops of wheat, with vineyards and fruit-orchards, are strung the ports of Oran, Mostaganem, Algiers,

Bougie, Philippeville and Bône (now Annaba). Algiers, the capital, has a population of 884,000. Cultivation, frequently with irrigation, is of a high standard and there is a considerable export of wine, fruit and vegetables. Between the coastal chains and the Saharan Atlas lies the plateau of the Shotts—named from its shallow evanescent lakes—an arid region of poor pasture supporting a mainly nomadic life. The eastern and western ends of the Atlas region, Tunisia and much of Morocco, were under French protection until 1956, and about half of their foreign trade is still with France.

Beyond the Atlas Mountains stretches the Algerian Sahara, divided into the departments of Ain-Sefra, Ghardaia, Oasis, and Touggourt, a rocky, sandy waste that is of great economic importance because of its oil and gas. Three large oilfields are in production (Edjélé, Hassi Massaoud and El Gassi), and natural gas is tapped at Djebel Berga and Hassi R'Mel. Supplies are pumped to Oran, Mostaganem, Algiers and Bougie (and also to Tunisia) and the bulk goes to France. The supplies are also contributing to the industrialization of Algeria, but Algeria remains France's leading trading partner in the Franc Zone both for imports and exports.

In French tropical Africa the native governments have inherited and are extending a number of irrigation enterprises, notably in Mali (French Sudan) where cotton and rice are grown in the bend of the Niger. Much of tropical Africa is a reservoir of raw materials for France, especially of vegetable oils. Foodstuffs account for half of all French purchases from the Franc Zone, while 75 per cent of her exports are manufactured goods. One of the advantages France offers to the African states is an association with the European Economic Community.

POPULATION OF PRINCIPAL TOWNS
(Census of 1962)

Paris, 2,790,000
Greater Paris, 7,400,000
Marseille, 780,000
Lyon, 530,000
Toulouse, 320,000
Nice, 290,000
Bordeaux, 250,000
Nantes, 240,000
Strasbourg, 230,000
St. Etienne, 201,000
Lille, 193,000
Le Havre, 184,000
Toulon, 162,000
Grenoble, 157,000
Rennes, 152,000
Brest, 136,000

Dijon, 136,000
Reims, 134,000
Le Mans, 132,000
Nancy, 129,000
Clermont-Ferrand, 128,000
Rouen, 121,000
Montpellier, 119,000
Limoges, 118,000
Angers, 115,000
Roubaix, 113,000
Mulhouse, 109,000
Boulogne, 107,000
Amiens, 105,000
Villeurbanne, 105,000
Metz, 103,000

NOTE ON THE EUROPEAN ECONOMIC
COMMUNITY (E.E.C.)

The bitter experiences of France in the first half of this century have led her to seek security along the logical path of a confederation of European states. Among the organizations established to this end was the Council of Europe, which has its headquarters at Strasbourg. The first practical move towards the creation of a European Community was the Schuman Plan for a common authority for Europe's coal and steel industries proposed in 1950. In 1952 France joined Italy, Germany and the Benelux countries (Belgium, Holland and Luxembourg) in establishing a Common Market for coal, iron and scrap, aimed at a gradual freeing of the movement of these commodities within the E.C.S.C. (The European Coal and Steel Community). As a result steel production in all six countries forged ahead. To the total steel production of E.C.S.C. in 1964 West Germany contributed 44 per cent and France 24 per cent. In 1958, with the setting up of the European Economic Community the principle of a Common Market was extended to all goods and at the same time a European Atomic Energy Authority (Euratom) was established. The next stage, the enlargement of the European Community to include other west European countries, would create a Common Market with a population of some 250,000,000 and a steel production not far behind that of the U.S.A. Up to the present attempts to bring other members of the Organization for Economic Co-operation and Development, including Britain, into the Common Market have been unsuccessful, but the E.E.C. has association agreements with Greece and Turkey and also with 18 African countries. Meanwhile, however, the E.E.C. has met with France's objection to implementing to the full the Rome Treaty, which she claims would violate her sovereignty. France fears the loss of her national identity, opposes a European Federation and thinks in terms of a "Europe des états"—

a confederation of states. The somewhat intransigent French attitude towards other organizations such as NATO and the United Nations is similarly based on a fear of losing the national independence for which she has fought through the centuries. French national consciousness is more deep-rooted than that of any other European country and she remains suspicious of a supra-national federal authority.

SHORT BIBLIOGRAPHY

AUGE-LARIBE, MICHEL. *La Révolution agricole*. Paris: Michel, 1955.

BAUM, WARREN CHARLES. *The French Economy and the State*. Princeton, N.J.: Princeton University Press, 1958.

BERTRAND, LEON. *Les grandes régions géologiques du sol français*. Paris: Flammarion, 1935.

BRAIBANT, MARCEL. *Vocation agricole de la France*. Paris: Berger-Levrault, 1959.

CLOUGH, SHEPHERD BANCROFT. *France: A History of National Economics, 1789–1939*. New York: Scribner, 1939.

DEMANGEON, ALBERT. *France économique et humaine*. (*Géographie universelle*, Vol. VI, Part 2.) 2 vols. Paris: Colin, 1948.

DUTTON, RALPH, and HOLDEN, ANGUS. *The Land of France*. New York: British Book Centre, 1953.

FAUCHER, DANIEL (ed.). *La France: géographie, tourisme*. 2 vols. Paris: Larousse, 1951–52.

FAUCHON, JEAN. *Economie de l'agriculture française*. Paris: Genin, 1954.

FIRTH, ALFRED. *French Life & Landscape*. 2 vols. London and New York: Elek, 1950–51.

FLEURE, H. J. *French Life and Its Problems*. London: Hachette, 1943.

France du demain. 8 vols. Paris: Presses Universitaires de France, 1959–62.

GOGUEL, JEAN. *Géologie de la France*. Paris: Presses Universitaires de France, 1950.

HOFFMANN, STANLEY, ET AL. *In Search of France.* Cambridge, Mass.: Harvard University Press, 1963.

LUTHY, HERBERT. *France Against Herself: A Perceptive Study of France's Past, Her Politics, and Her Unending Crises.* New York: Praeger, 1955.

MADARIAGA, SALVADOR DE. *Englishmen, Frenchmen, and Spaniards.* London: Oxford University Press, 1928.

MARTONNE, EMMANUEL DE. *The Geographical Regions of France.* London: Heinemann, 1933.

———. *France Physique. (Géographie universelle,* Vol. VI, Part 1.) Paris: Colin, 1947.

MIROT, LEON. *Manuel de géographie historique de la France.* 2 vols. Paris: Picard, 1947–50.

MONKHOUSE, F. J. *The Geography of Northwestern Europe.* New York: Praeger, 1966.

ORMSBY, HILDA R. *France: A Regional and Economic Geography.* Rev. ed. London: Methuen, 1950.

PINCHEMEL, PH. *Géographie de la France.* 2 vols. Paris: Colin, 1964.

SHACKLETON, MARGARET REID. *Europe: A Regional Geography.* 7th ed. New York: Praeger, 1965.

SIEGFRIED, ANDRE. *France: A Study in Nationality.* London: Oxford University Press, 1930.

TRACY, MICHAEL. *Agriculture in Western Europe.* New York: Praeger, 1964.

VIDAL DE LA BLACHE, PAUL. *Tableau de la géographie de la France. (Histoire de France,* ed. Ernest Lavisse, Vol. I, Part 1.) Paris: Hachette, 1922.

———. *The Personality of France.* London: Christophers, 1928.

WRIGHT, GORDON. *Rural Revolution in France: The Peasantry in the Twentieth Century.* Stanford, Calif.: Stanford University Press, 1964.

Informative pamphlets on many aspects of French life can be obtained on request from the Press and Information Division, French Embassy, 972 Fifth Avenue, New York, N. Y. 10021.

INDEX

Plate I

VÉZELAY

Ancient hill-town on the southern edge of the Paris Basin, famous in the Middle Ages as a monastic centre and place of pilgrimage. Its Abbey Church is a celebrated product of the Burgundy school of Romanesque twelfth-century architecture. (See p. 75.)

Plate II

CHARTRES

A typical settlement of the Paris Basin, dominated by its great Gothic Cathedral. The old town stands on a low hill, formerly protected by ramparts, overlooking the River Eure and the plains of Beauce.

ARLES

A town of Roman heritage in South France. The Roman monuments (amphitheatre and arena) stand out boldly among the massed houses of the town. The River Rhône is in the background.

Plate III

HUEZ

An Alpine village, nearly 5,000 feet above sea, famous for its fine pastures and for the cheese produced by the transhumant flocks which gather here in summer. Notice the snow-covered Alp in the middle distance, the glacial cirques, and the over-deepened valleys. Notice also the steep shingled roofs of the houses.

LAKE BOURGET

Lying in one of the deep transverse "cluses" of the limestone pre-Alps, a focus of attraction in a region of difficulty. Prehistoric lake-dwellers occupied its shores and the fashionable Aix-les-Bains is a town of Roman origin.

Plate IV

Demangeon

CÔTE DES MAURES

*The broken coast of Provence, east of Toulon, where the ancient rocks
of the Maures, clothed in pine and evergreen oak,
meet the Mediterranean.*

MARKET-GARDENING IN THE SUBURBS OF
PARIS AT CHÂTILLON

*Each plot of ground yields several crops a year under
intensive hand cultivation.*

Plate V

BEAUCE

The heart of the Paris Basin. Open fields of the fertile treeless plains between Paris and Orléans. The large farms, each with its tree-sheltered enclosure of pasture, are strung along the roads, not grouped in villages.

THE SITE OF PARIS

The nucleus of the city, showing the Ile de la Cité, with Notre-Dame Cathedral, and the many bridges which use the island as a crossing place.

Plate VI

TRÉGUIER

An ancient settlement of Côtes-du-Nord, Brittany. The drowned valley or ria gives access to the sea, and the port was formerly very active. A typical view of coastal Armorica.

NANCY

One of France's regional capitals; Place Stanislas, the centre of the city, a famous example of eighteenth-century architecture and planning.

Plate VII

CAHORS

*Surrounded on three sides by the River Lot, which is crossed by the
fortified Pont Valentré. One of the route and market-towns
at the edge of the Central Plateau.*

THE TARN GORGE

*One of the deep gorges cut into the limestones of the Central Plateau
by the tributaries of the Garonne. In many of the cliffs thus
formed prehistoric man made his habitations.*

Plate VIII

P. George

INTENSIVE CULTIVATION IN THE PLAINS OF VAUCLUSE

*Notice the rows of cypress trees and the reed-fences
for protection against the Mistral.*

MARSEILLE

*The modern port, sheltered behind a long breakwater. In the fore-
ground is the old harbour, around which clusters the
ancient town dominated by the cathedral.*